Their Silent Message

Books by Elizabeth Bowne

GIFT FROM THE AFRICAN HEART

THEIR SILENT MESSAGE

Their Silent Message

by ELIZABETH BOWNE

McGRAW-HILL BOOK COMPANY

New York Toronto London Sydney

THEIR SILENT MESSAGE

Library of Congress Catalog Card Number: 68-18574
First Edition 06820

To my son Frank, with the humble hope that he might join the many who, in the years ahead, will respond to the silent message of humanity.

Their Silent Message

One

DURING THE NIGHT the rains came, falling quickly and sharply like spears attacking the tin roof. I lay in bed, shrouded in a mosquito net, in a little house deep in the jungle of Liberia, West Africa. A damp breeze stirred at the window, rattling the aluminum blinds drawn against the dark outside. The light from the lantern left burning on the floor beside my bed splashed eerie shadows against the walls. And the smell of kerosene mingled with the musty odor of the lonely room.

Only that afternoon I had arrived by small plane, flying with a Lutheran mission pilot from the capital city of Monrovia on the coast to the hinterland village of Sanoyea. I was revisiting the tiny jungle village after ten years. Now as I thought of how the new experiences of those years were linked to the old memories of my past visit, it seemed that my return had been predestined. Yet I lay in a mysterious gloom, weary from my long journey, unable to sleep. Even if I opened my eyes, the weird patterns from the lantern light seemed to flicker and sway on the walls that surrounded me, making me more restless still.

Suddenly I heard someone coming around the house and then a call at the window of the room where the German-born Lutheran nurse, who was my hostess, slept.

"Sister Lena," the voice called again.

I looked out and saw a man standing in the rain, a lantern in his hand.

"I'll be right along," I heard the nurse say, and in a few moments she came to my door.

"My night watchman has called me for a delivery," she said.

I sat up in bed.

"Since you came all the way to Sanoyea to see my work in the new dispensary," she added, a firmness in her voice, "you might as well start learning right now."

"It must be the middle of the night," I said, rubbing my eyes.

"It's past one o'clock," she said. "Are you coming?"

I pushed back the mosquito netting and in the dull lantern light I saw that she already wore her grey uniform which hung almost to her ankles. With one hand she adjusted a pin in her grey-brown hair, which she had twisted into a knot at the back of her head. With the other hand she held a lantern. Her face looked pale but her eyes seemed alert.

"Hurry up," she said. "And bring your lantern."

I dressed quickly and followed her out onto the porch. I still felt dazed from lack of sleep. But she seemed completely wide awake and kept talking about her work as we picked our way through the rain, along the path.

"The women who came here for delivery are lucky," she said briskly. "I urge them to come as soon as they think they are pregnant and to keep coming regularly for prenatal care."

We crossed the road. "Also I make them stay in the dispensary for at least four days after their baby arrives."

I rushed to keep up with her.

"I charge them only three dollars for the whole thing," she

went on. "That's reasonable enough, wouldn't you say?"

I nodded.

"But I have to make sure they pay all of it at the very beginning," she said, pausing to step over a puddle, "otherwise they might stop coming."

"Why?" I asked as we went up the steps into the dispensary.

But she left my question unanswered.

Stopping on the steps, she held up her lantern and pointed to a grey metal plaque on the wall beside the door. "I guess that will mean something special to you," she said, a sudden quietness in her voice.

Standing there in the rain I read:

This Dispensary Dedicated to
The People of Sanoyea
In Remembrance of Their
Noble Efforts
June 22, 1951
Given In Memory of the
"Great Republic"
Plane Victims

I stood there trembling and for a moment I could not move. Coming back to Sanoyea had brought back a flood of sad memories. But now seeing this sign I felt overwhelmed.

Sister Lena turned to me. "The people give you credit for the new dispensary," she said. "Come," she added, pushing past the night watchman who stood now at the door with his lantern.

We went through the large waiting room filled with empty benches. Then I followed her through the consulting office and on into the delivery room.

"Miss Yunger," Sister Lena addressed an African girl in a

nurse's uniform. "I hope you haven't called me too soon."

The young nurse, tall and slender with an attractive though solemn face, stood beside the delivery table. Sister Lena explained to me that the girl was from a different tribe in another part of Liberia and had been trained at a mission hospital and sent to Sanoyea to serve as her assistant. The young nurse did not speak during this discussion of her. Only once she flashed a glance at me, a look that seemed to express pride coupled with dejection.

Then she turned and bent over the expectant mother. "Her time is near," she said quietly.

The woman, nude and swollen, lay on her back on the delivery table. Her arms and legs were thin and bony, her eyes drawn with pain.

Crowded to one side of the room a young girl stood with four older women. "This is Nohi," said Sister Lena, indicating the girl. "She is the interpreter for these women who have come here from the bush for a three months' training course as midwives." Printed turbans covered their hair, and they looked neat with white aprons over the tribal dresses wrapped around their bodies. With expressionless faces they nodded to me.

The door to the linen closet stood open and I saw a young woman searching on the shelves in the semidarkness.

"Helen," Sister Lena called to her, "do you have the baby clothes ready?"

"Yes, ma'am," she answered and she stepped from the closet carrying a baby's shirt and a diaper. Dark and of medium height, she moved slowly, and there was something quiet yet deliberate in her nature.

A window on the outside wall was covered with an aluminum blind. A door on the right opened into a tiny bathroom. On the left another doorway led into a hall.

Besides the delivery table there was an examination table

and a smaller table on which there sat a lantern and a bucket of boiled water. Two chairs were pushed back against one wall and across from them stood a cabinet filled with medicines. On top of the cabinet there sat a wash basin, a bar of soap, and a bottle of Lysol.

Sister Lena washed her hands and then stood beside the mother. The woman did not cry out but her face grimaced with the pain of struggle.

"You must save your energy," Sister Lena scolded. "Do not strain at the wrong time."

The woman remained calm for a moment, then almost immediately her body twisted, wracked with pain.

"Stop straining," warned the nurse.

The woman gritted her teeth and her whole body shuddered.

"If you don't do as I tell you," Sister Lena said sternly, "I can't help you."

Nurse Yunger stood at the other side of the bed, her eyes cast down, dispirited. The women and the girl, still with expressionless faces, watched quietly from across the room. I heard Helen sigh. The mother bit her lip, her whole body tense with pain, yet hardly a sound came from her throat. The lantern light flickered. Outside the rain beat down on the tin roof.

Suddenly the mother screamed and the top half of the baby's head appeared.

"Stop screaming and push now, push hard," Sister Lena ordered. But the mother fell back almost in a faint.

"You must push," scolded the nurse, trying to grasp the baby's head. But she could not get a grip on it. "Push," she repeated. And then in her frustration she lashed out, "you must help, or had you rather be having this baby out in the bush?"

The woman lay there limp, shaking her head.

"Push, push, I tell you," the nurse cried.

As the woman struggled in her pain I felt my fingernails pressing into the skin of my tightly clasped hands.

"Push, I tell you," shouted the nurse, still unable to get a grasp on the baby's head.

The woman leaned up and tried to cooperate, but then she let out a piercing scream and fell back.

"Stop that screaming," cried the nurse, "and do as I tell you."

But the woman lay back limp as if her strength were completely gone now.

"No," the nurse shouted, trying to rally the woman.

I thought she had passed out but as Sister Lena shook her, she opened her eyes slowly as if using her last bit of strength.

The nurse, her face red with determination and wet with perspiration, shouted again. "I cannot do the whole job. You must cooperate!"

The woman moved her lips but no sound came from them.

Desperately the nurse tried to grasp the baby's head. "A little more," she pleaded, "push, push—do you hear?"

But the mother did not move except for two large tears that rolled out of her eyes and drained down her cheeks.

The rain slowed to a drizzle on the roof. The aluminum blind banged at the window and then became still. For a few moments the room, stifling with the odor of Lysol, was starkly silent like a warning of death. In the nurse's eyes I saw the fear that the new life would be suffocated if delivery was delayed any longer.

"Push," cried the nurse, and in the silence the word hung as if it were a final desperate demand.

The woman clasped her fingers into fists, wrinkled her brow and clenched her jaw, but despite every effort no power showed in her body.

Instantly, Nurse Yunger was up on the bed on her knees beside the mother. With her hands firmly against the woman's stomach she pushed with all her strength. The mother's face wrenched out of shape as she tried not to scream. And then she gasped for breath, screamed wildly, and the whole head of the baby was out. Quickly Sister Lena brought forth the child—a boy, large and perfectly formed. But it did not seem to be alive.

Sister Lena held it up by its feet and tapped it on its back. Still no sound. Working quickly, she laid it on the delivery table, there between the mother's legs, and reached for the syringe that Nurse Yunger handed to her. Forcing open the mouth of the infant she captured mucus from its throat. Rushing to the bucket of clean boiled water, Helen dipped some out into a bowl and brought it to Sister Lena, who plunged her fingers into the water and then sprinkled it into the face of the baby.

The midwife trainees, who had delivered many children in their own way in the bush, stood poised, a fierce look on their faces now, as if ready to take over if the nurse failed.

Suddenly the baby, a strange shade of grey in the flickering lantern light, whimpered and then cried out.

The nurse stepped back, sighed, and wiped the perspiration from her face. "Take him," she said to Helen, and then she turned away. Although she had saved his life she seemed to be unmoved.

But Helen picked him up gently and took him to another table to clean and dress him.

Sister Lena turned to me. "Some of the women are very difficult," she said wearily.

When she had finished with the mother and carefully examined the placenta she pointed across the hall to a small room in the back. Then she stood aside while the woman slowly struggled up off the delivery table, and bent over with exhaustion, shuffled into the smaller room.

"Some of the women are very difficult," the nurse repeated as she shook her head.

Instead of answering her I followed the mother and I watched as she pulled herself up into one of the two empty beds, the only furniture in the room. I stood beside her and saw her matted hair, the perspiration on her forehead, her body flat and strangely emaciated now. I wanted to say something to her, some word of comfort or understanding, but I felt so overwhelmed by all I had witnessed that I could not speak.

She lay back and stared up at me with a look that for a moment would not let me go, a long searching look that seemed to come from deep within. Still unable to speak, I put my hand against her arm. She said nothing, yet as she glanced away and then back at me it seemed that she spoke to me, as one heart to another.

When I returned to the delivery room Nurse Yunger and Helen were putting things in order while Nohi and the four women cleaned and straightened the room. Sister Lena spoke to the midwives who had come for the three months' training course.

"I hope you have learned something tonight about how to handle a difficult delivery," she said.

They stared blankly at her.

"Tell our visitor," she said to the tallest one, "how you would have delivered this baby in the bush."

From an expressionless face the old woman's eyes blinked. Then folding her arms and speaking through the girl Nohi, who acted as the interpreter, she began to explain that when she delivered a baby she always stood at the mother's feet and braced herself by grasping the mother's hands and placing her own foot against the mother's rectum.

"Her own foot, bare and dirty," Sister Lena emphasized.

The woman nodded.

"But why?" I asked.

"To keep the baby from coming out the wrong place," she said.

I looked at Sister Lena, disbelieving.

"Yes," she said, "that's what they do."

The old woman went on. "If the mother have a long hard time, like this woman, I get a stick and beat her."

"Beat her?" I exclaimed. "Why?"

" 'Cause I know she done some awful sinful thing that provoke the spirits and they make her suffer."

"I don't understand," I said.

Sister Lena glanced at me, her sad eyes more distressed than usual.

The old woman continued. "I got to beat her 'til she tell what bad thing she done." She bobbed her head and as she talked the corners of her turban worked loose over each ear. "Then maybe I can get the spirit to go 'way and leave her 'lone."

I stared at the woman, her worn, wrinkled face, her turban that stood out wildly now from each side of her head. Her black piercing eyes seemed to hold all the mystery of the bush, of life unreal.

"Yes," Sister Lena said, "I have seen women with great welts across their stomachs and backs. Sometimes they have come here almost beaten to death."

Nurse Yunger frowned and I could see that her inherent pride made her resent the exposure of the ignorance of the native people. Quickly she finished her work and without saying a word to anyone she went out. I looked at Helen. "Yes," she said sadly, "what the woman tells is true."

I turned back to the old woman. "When the baby come," she went on, "I catch it and cut its cord with my jungle knife."

"Would you have washed your hands or boiled the knife?" Sister Lena asked.

"No," she confessed. "I not use any water except to wash the baby."

"And what about the afterbirth?" the nurse prompted.

"I pull it right out," said the old woman.

"And quite often a piece gets left inside and causes the mother to bleed to death," Sister Lena said with dismay. She shook her head. "Is there any wonder that the infant mortality rate in some areas is as high as 70 percent?"

"That's incredible!"

"Yes, but I'm changing that," she said proudly. "In the five years I have been here I have trained over fifty midwives, having three or four come for three months at a time."

In the dull light her face glowed bright with achievement. "These women have been here about a month." Then, addressing the women, she added, "Tell Mrs. Bowne what you have learned."

One of the women spoke up. "We must always wash our hands before we touch the mother. We must not strike the mother no matter how long she groans or how loud she screams. We must never, never pull out the afterbirth before it ready to come."

Sister Lena smiled. "It's a beginning," she said. "Before I let them make a delivery they must be able to repeat every detail correctly."

I thought of the difficulty involved. The women, completely illiterate, must learn through the girl Nohi's translation. And it was obvious that Nohi had difficulty grasping Sister Lena's English, which was spoken with a heavy German accent.

The nurse, standing aside, watched the women closely as they moved about the room, hesitating at each task, still unsure and out of place in their strange environment.

Finally when they were finished she turned to me. "Come," she said, picking up her lantern. "Let's go back to the house where we can sit down to talk."

Sitting in her living room in the dim lantern light, the nurse told me how she began her midwife training program. "When I learned how many mothers and babies died at the hands of those bush women," she said, "I decided that something drastic had to be done. I wrote a note to the District Commissioner and told him that he should order every Paramount Chief in this area to send all midwives here for training."

"That was a large undertaking for you," I said.

"Yes," she said, "but it was necessary."

"No doubt it has saved many lives," I said, "and it must have been a rewarding experience for you."

"I couldn't do it all at once," she said, "but a start had to be made."

She folded her arms and went on. "I explained that I would provide a hut for the women but that each one must bring her own food. While they are here I insist that they witness every birth, day or night."

Her face was stern as she spoke, with the same look of authority that I had seen in the dispensary. "I promised that they would receive a certificate at the end of three months if they learned well," she said, "and if not, they would be sent back to the bush empty-handed."

A damp breeze blew from the window making the lantern light blink. "I've had to send some away after only a few days," she went on, "because they just didn't seem to understand anything."

Despite the lateness of the hour Sister Lena sat up straight as she talked. "Once I dismissed my whole class of four women only one week before they were to graduate."

"Why?" I asked.

Her jaw angled, bringing an adamant look to her face. "They were supposed to care for a woman who had just given birth, but they were neglectful and the woman almost bled to death. She would have died too if I hadn't gone back and checked her just in time."

"That's too bad," I said, "but surely you offered to give the women another chance?"

"Why should I?"

"Perhaps they didn't understand," I said, "what with the difficulty of the language and . . ."

"Oh, no," she insisted, "I have to be firm with these people. It's the only way to teach them anything."

I watched her, wondering about her obvious concern for the people, and yet what seemed to me a certain lack of compassion. She leaned back in her chair. As she went on talking, she fingered the silver cross, a symbol of the deaconess order, that hung at her neck.

The rain still sprinkled on the roof and as I listened I heard it running down the chimney. I looked at the fireplace and saw a puddle of water in the ashes. A gust of wind from the window sent the lantern light dancing wildly across the wall. Then in a moment of stillness, from the distance, I heard a bird cry.

My thoughts returned to the scene in the dispensary, to the screams of pain, then to the silence of the baby as it wavered on the edge of life, and the silence in the dark eyes of the mother after her physical pain was gone and she lay in the small room alone. And I thought of my journey from New York and the reasons that had brought me back to this place.

Was it only twelve hours ago that the little mission plane had rolled to a stop on the grassy landing strip just beyond the village of Sanoyea?

Two

WHEN I STEPPED from the plane I was amazed to see hundreds of African villagers waiting. They stood grouped together at the end of the grass strip, as if presenting to me a human fortress of protection from the jungle beyond. Also, standing to one side, three white missionaries waited.

I was greeted first by Sister Lena Jurgens, the tall, greying nurse who had strong angular features and a firm handshake. Yet I noticed that her eyes seemed sad, distant, almost questioning. I had corresponded with her to make arrangements for my visit, and as she lived alone she had invited me to stay at her house.

Next a pretty young woman with long brown hair offered me her hand. "Hello," she said, "I'm Marcia Anderson." She introduced me to her husband Erwin, a slender, attractive man with close-cropped light hair and a friendly smile. The young couple, also Lutherans, and the nurse comprised the total white mission staff for the small village of about a thousand people.

After I greeted them, Sister Lena turned my attention to the waiting Africans. "It was the villagers' own idea to walk all the way out here to meet you," she said, indicating the crowd.

"I told them only that you were coming here to visit the mission."

She led me then to a tall native who waited in the center of the large group of villagers. "This is Chief Momo Kaine," she said. "He has been Paramount Chief of this area for the past two years."

The African man stood straight, his body draped in a handsome black and white robe. On his head he wore a round gold and white ceremonial hat. His skin was dark, his features smooth and even, his face solemn. He nodded and studied me with his large gentle eyes. "Welcome to Sanoyea," he said.

Then he in turn, as Paramount Chief, introduced me to his tribal chiefs, clan chiefs, and town chiefs, many of whom, I learned later, he had summoned from great distances for my arrival.

The people glanced down as if wishing to show special reverence for the occasion. Humbly I shook each hand and heard their simple words of greeting. The sun blinked in and out between the clouds as if spotlighting the men in their colorful robes and the women in their bright wrappers. Kind, solemn faces surrounded me in the quiet. No sound came from the bush around us. And as I moved among them I felt caught up in a sense of oneness, which in that moment seemed to bind me to the jungle folk. While I did not recognize any of them from my previous visit I felt that most of them recognized me. I studied each face, aware somehow that they shared my sense of silent communication.

Finally, the chief spoke again. "We thank you for coming," he said, "and we wish to carry you to Sister Lena's home on the mission compound, the long way around, through the village."

I saw the hammock then, woven of vine. A bright cloth had been draped over the top to shield out the rain or the sun.

Four strong boys, two at each end of the hammock, balanced it carefully on their heads.

I looked at the nurse for her approval.

"You must go with them," Sister Lena said. "They insist on honoring you in this way."

Turning, she followed the Andersons to a Land Rover parked near a narrow road that led into the bush.

The Africans gathered closer around me then, and the four boys stooped down low for me to get into the hammock. As soon as I lay back in the vine net they moved off immediately, with Chief Kaine leading the way. He walked down the grassy landing strip, past the road cut for the Land Rover, to a narrow path that opened into the bush.

At first everyone remained silent except for a few older men who stepped up to caution the hammock boys to be careful. After we entered the bush I heard only the sound of hundreds of bare feet treading softly on the dirt as the line of villagers stretched out in single file behind the hammock.

Big damp leaves, branches, and the tangled greenery pressed in on either side of the swinging net. The bright blue- and red-flowered cloth draped overhead shielded out the sun, and only occasionally when the path widened did I catch a glimpse of the sky with its misty clouds. There seemed to be no life in the jungle around us, and in the quiet I heard the heavy breathing of the hammock boys, who moved at a rhythmic pace.

Suddenly we stopped and Chief Kaine spoke to the boys. "Be careful here," he said. "I will guide you."

I raised my head to see what was happening. We had come to a stream with a single log stretched across it. While the boys waded on either side, the chief crossed the log, half turned so that he could guide the hammock himself. I felt the hammock sink down as the boys waded in dark water over their knees.

But the water did not touch me, and soon we were on the other side.

Each time we came to a stream, obviously swollen from a recent rain, the chief showed his concern, and the boys, without missing a step, waded through rushing water, taking me across safely. I lay back in the swinging hammock and closed my eyes. In the quietness I felt as if I were drifting through space.

Time passed, perhaps only ten or fifteen or twenty minutes. But it became for me time eternal in which I seemed to move, with the rhythm of the swinging net, away from myself, on and on and on. And as I did I seemed to see an endless line of people, their voices hushed, their despondent eyes turned to me. They marched slowly, moving from all the corners of the earth, surrounding me. I felt drawn to them, tightly embraced somehow by this strange visionary scene. And not until much later, as the days of my visit passed, did I begin to understand its meaning.

The reverent mood in which the people greeted me cast a spell and this mystique remained unbroken until the path ended and we entered the edge of the village. Then an old man, apparently the merry-maker of the town, appeared and danced along beside the hammock, singing and calling out to make everyone laugh. The people crowded around me and began to chant in their tribal tongue a cheerful singsong rhythm. Beyond them I caught a glimpse of a girl who threw open a shuttered window and another who stood in an open doorway to smile and wave.

An old woman with flat dangling breasts turned from her cooking pot and called out a greeting. Another, winnowing rice, stopped to watch. A small boy rolled a rusty wheel, running to keep up with the hammock carriers. A baby, startled by the noise and confusion, looked up from sucking at his mother's breast and blinked at me. Children trotted alongside of the hammock, giggled with friendly delight, reached out to touch me, and called, "Howdy, Mama, howdy plenty."

We moved, as a multitude, beyond the village, past the mission church. Inside the edge of the mission compound the carriers soon swung to the right. In a few moments they stopped, between two large trees, at a gate. Sitting up I realized that we had arrived at the home of the nurse. Sister Lena came down the short path from the house. The chanting ceased and the people stood by quietly.

The chief helped me from the hammock. For a moment I stood dazed from the jouncing and swinging of the net and from the strange reverie through which I had passed. Then when I glanced up I saw the people, silent now, pressed around me. As I looked out into their gentle faces and their somber eyes, I felt overwhelmed by their kindness. For a moment I stood there groping for words.

Finally I turned to Chief Kaine. "Thank you," I managed. Then I shook hands with the hammock boys, noticing the muscles in their bare arms and the perspiration that drained down their necks.

The nurse stepped up. "Come inside now," she said, taking me by the arm.

"Chief Kaine," she called back over her shoulder, "would you like to join us for a cup of tea?"

He nodded and followed us up the path. The house, a yellow stucco bungalow, was new since my previous visit. It had a screened front porch, two bedrooms, a bath, a combination living-dining room, a kitchen, a large pantry, and a storage area. The living room was furnished with practical modern furniture. Short blue curtains hung limp at the windows. A large cement cross protruded from the wall over the fireplace.

By the time the Andersons came in to join us the crowd

outside had dispersed, except for the children whose curiosity seemed to make them linger on.

We sat at the dining table, which was covered with a white linen cloth. A bowl of wild flowers arranged in the center of the table added color. We drank tea from plastic cups and ate bread, butter, jam, and cheese, brought in by a shy, solemn girl from the kitchen.

"How long have you worked here?" I asked the nurse.

"I have been here in Sanoyea for five years," said Sister Lena, and she went on to explain that she had immigrated from Germany to the United States after World War II. Later she had volunteered at the mission headquarters in New York to come to Africa to serve.

Pouring the tea she added, "The Andersons are native Americans but they have been here less than a year."

Marcia smiled. "We both are from the Midwest," she said, "and we were married soon after we finished school."

"This is our first mission post," said Erwin as he spread butter on a piece of toast.

"What is your work here?" I asked him.

"I'm an agriculturist," he answered. "But I must spend this first year learning the local Kpelle language."

"I wanted to learn the language," said the nurse, "but I have never had the time."

The Andersons exchanged a glance. There was an awkward silence and then the chief spoke. "I have heard about your last visit to our village," he said to me. "I am sorry I was in Monrovia at the time and we did not meet."

"I am surprised that the villagers remember me," I said.

"Oh, yes," he said, "they all remember you."

As we sipped our tea and talked, I studied the faces of the others who sat with me. I felt a strange tenseness between them as if each one waited for the other to speak.

"Have many things changed here in the past ten years?" I asked.

The Andersons shrugged their shoulders and said they did not know. Sister Lena spoke firmly. "I have changed some things that badly needed changing."

She sat up straighter. "Isn't that right, Chief?"

Chief Kaine nodded but did not speak.

When the nurse turned her attention to refilling the cups with tea, the chief glanced up at me. "Still we have great needs," he said, "for many things have hardly changed at all."

"The new dispensary has made quite some difference," remarked the nurse.

"Yes," the chief said with appreciation.

"Tell me about the new dispensary," I said, thinking of the long years I had waited and the great distance I had traveled to see it.

Sister Lena sighed and shook her head. "You will see all the work it involves soon enough," she said.

I wanted to visit the new building immediately but before I could press the issue the chief rose. "The people want to dance for you," he said. "Will you come with me?"

We followed him into the village. Many children of different sizes waited in front of the house and they walked with us. Some of the smallest ones wore only strings around their waists or beads dangling at their necks. Others were completely nude. Older boys wore little shirts that barely covered their hips. A few girls had pieces of bright fabric tied around themselves like diapers. Not many wore dresses. The taller girls, some perhaps only eight or nine years old, minded their baby brothers or sisters by carrying them on their backs. The children looked up at me with dark solemn eyes.

As we walked, I could see all the things that I had not seen clearly from the swinging hammock. We passed the sturdy stone and frame mission church which stood on our left. The wooden framing looked weathered and badly in need of paint.

In the village I saw that some of the mud huts had new tin roofs, but from most of them ragged thatch still hung down from the spiraled framework. One rectangular house with a wooden door had several shuttered windows. Another hut, small and round, had no windows. At the next house, on an earthen extension sheltered by the thatch overhang, an old woman squatted beside a little iron pot hung over a cooking fire. The smell of smoke lingered with us as we walked on.

We passed a square hut, with a wide opening across the front, used as a store. From the path I could see a few tins of meat, fruit and milk, bolts of printed cloth tawdry in design and color. There was a barrel of rice and one of peanuts, some cassava roots, bananas, papayas, and dried red peppers. From the door frame furs, skins, animal horns, feathers, and dried bits of animal intestines hung down. Flies clung to a chain of bones and somewhere from inside there came an odor of herbs mingled with the smell of drying blood.

We followed the wide dirt street, which had looked clean from the air, when the small plane had circled the village, but eroded in places where heavy rains had washed it away. We stepped over puddles and edged around areas of deep mud. Overhead the sun peered between the lumpy white clouds that drifted low out of the deep blue sky. Surrounding the village like a fringe, the palms, banana bushes, and other greenery contrasted with the drab browns of the thatched roofs, the mud huts, and the wet ground.

Because they are afraid of the many poisonous snakes from the jungle, the people never allow grass to grow near their homes. I remembered this from my previous visit; yet I was surprised again by the appearance of austerity that this necessary rule brings.

As we passed a hut I saw a calla lily with one red blossom, tall and alone, planted beside a doorway. Growing there in the stark drabness of its surroundings it seemed almost unreal. I paused to examine it and I thought of how in its brilliance it was like a sign of hope in this land.

In front of a house in the center of the village, homemade raffia chairs were set out for us. A large crowd had gathered. Everyone waited in the sun, colorful in their striped country cloth robes and bright printed wrappers. Two drummers stood to one side with four men and one girl, the chorus or chanters who sang to the drummers' rhythm.

A man who seemed to be in charge held up a long stick and with it drew a circle on the ground to indicate the dancing area. The people pressed close around the circle, bare toes bordering on the line. The chief led me to the chair nearest the music makers who had begun to drum and chant in the local Kpelle language.

But no one danced.

I turned to Chief Kaine and asked him to draw his chair closer beside me. Trying to speak above the din of musical sounds I asked him why no one danced.

"They will," he said. "They need more time."

I did not understand, but I turned back to watch the chanters. The men wore pants and shirts, and the girl wore a bright pink dress closely fitted to her curved figure. Their arms hung loosely at their sides. As they sang, a deep seriousness showed on their faces. Their eyes seemed to stare out beyond the crowd as if searching far into the depths of time.

"Please," I said to the chief, "tell me what they are saying, what their song is about."

He folded his arms across his chest, and leaning back he nodded. "They are recalling great dancers from our past," he said, "telling of their power and skill."

Chief Kaine kept nodding as he listened. "Soon they will

call on someone in the crowd," he went on, "and ask that person to try to dance as well, to bring honor to our people."

The crowd stood impassive, yet attentive to the words of the chanters. As I watched, a tall man in a dull grey shirt shook his head, mumbled something, and moved back in the crowd.

"They have called on that man," said the chief, "but he says he isn't ready."

The girl in the pink dress clapped her hands now in rhythm with the drummers. She sang out quite loudly while the other chanters hummed. Her face wore an expression of deep longing.

"What is she saying?" I asked the chief.

He watched her and at the end of each phrase he translated. "My lover has gone, far away, very far away, beyond the trees, and the hills, and the streams that flood our land. So long he has been gone. Many times the rains have come. Hungry time has passed again and again and still he has not returned. When will my lover come back to me? When will I see his smiling face, his muscles, his body big and strong?"

The chief looked at me and laughed, a bit embarrassed by the girl's lament.

Again she sang, a pleading wail streaming from her throat, the cry of the desperation of the lonely, the forgotten. Then she paused and a light seemed to turn on in her eyes.

The chief translated. "I will dance," she says. "I will dance to bring him back."

Suddenly she jumped into the circle, her feet flying in a frenzy, her eyes rolled back, every movement of her body sensual as the excitement mounted. For a few moments she remained lost in her dream. Then as if the elastic of reality snapped back, she ducked her head, giggled, and fled into the crowd.

Next a young man looking remarkably western in long

white trousers, a white shirt, and a white jungle helmet moved into the circle. His bare feet raised the dust and, despite his western clothes, with this dance he seemed to rejoin the spirits of the past. The white helmet he tossed in his hand might have been a spear. The power and cunning of his ancestors came alive.

One after another, young men dressed in colorful native robes and with their hair clipped short entered the ring to show their fancy footwork and live for a few brief moments within some personal dream. Little by little, as if overcoming some deep pain, their drama built. The people called out encouragement to the dancers, and as each one gave what he could of himself, a shout of cheer rose for him.

In the crowd a mood seemed to grow from the ground. Feet became restless, then hips swayed, shoulders moved, murmurs escaped from open lips, and eyes that knew past suffering brightened somehow, aware of the message of the drum that gathered them in. The sun slipped down a little in the west, throwing long shadows on the dancers and on the features of those who watched. The chief sighed, a look of understanding on his face.

A boy in a red shirt and blue pants eased his way through the crowd to the edge of the circle. He stood first on one foot and then the other, looking around aimlessly as if in search of an elusive inspiration. Then suddenly he leaped into the ring dancing with skill and precision and unbelievable vigor. After him there came a shy girl, wearing an orange plaid wrapper pulled up barely enough to cover her breast. Her dance was more of a shuffle, a pensive search. An old man danced as if in an effort to regain his youth. The girl in the pink dress reappeared. She patted her foot and clapped her hands and sang out louder than ever now. Small children followed adults into the circle trying to imitate their steps.

Perspiration soaked the shirts of the drummers. A slight breeze stirred the air as the sun sank down a bit more behind the jungle wall. But the people never did dance as a group. Rather, caught up by some inspiration, each one danced alone, not for entertainment it seemed, but as an expression of some deep need. I felt it was a solemn occasion to be viewed with reverence.

With the relentless drumming crowding in on me I felt the restlessness of the dancers as their feet moved back and forth stirring the dust, carrying them first one way and then another. Did they seek some kind of release, or were they reaching for some kind of hope?

I thought then of my own restlessness that ten years before had first brought me to this land. At the time that the commercial airliner carried my pilot husband and all the forty persons aboard to their deaths, when it fell on a hilltop in the jungle beyond Sanoyea, I had been in New York. Seven months later our son, an only child, was born. When he was two months old I had left him with my sister and had traveled to this remote spot on the map to visit my husband's grave. Although I was quite young, a shy Georgia girl reared on the family plantation handed down from my slave-owning ancestors, and I had great trepidation about going to Africa, I had somehow determined to make that trip, for I had felt a great need, not only to understand the circumstances concerning the death of my husband, but also to search for some new meaning for my life . . . some new faith to live by.

I thought of the solace I had gained from some of the people of Sanoyea as they reached out to me with patience and human kindness. Then I had learned of how the native people themselves had suffered when the tragedy struck their village, for the mission people who were there at the time had prevailed upon them to bring the bodies of the plane victims down the hill for burial in the new cemetery beyond the mission compound. Not only was this a very difficult task during the rainy season when a steep path had to be hacked out of the jungle, but the people had to defy their chief who at that time was a man named Peter Giddings. He had warned them that the evil spirits that caused the plane to fall might attack them. Fear of the evil spirits had gripped the minds and hearts of the people. Yet they had done the grim task for a simple reason. A young girl, who had cared for my room when I was there before, had explained it to me. "We did it," she had said, " 'cause we cry for folks everywhere."

As I had turned from my own suffering to a greater awareness of theirs, I wanted to do something to help them. Finally I had determined to find a way to replace their inadequate little log dispensary with a more permanent building where greater medical care could be offered to the people. Such a building would stand in memory of the dead and for the better health of the living.

Yet how slowly the idea for such a memorial had grown after my previous visit. I thought of how difficult it had been even to get a list of the next of kin of the plane victims, for the airlines clung to the strange fear that I might use it for some other purpose, although what that purpose could be was never made clear.

I remembered the weeks I had spent writing letters to the next of kin once I had secured the list from the missionary who gained it to write letters of condolence. With the answers there had come donations large and small. Then as the memorial fund grew, the women of the United Lutheran Church of America had contributed the final amount needed to make the building possible.

I thought of the years I had waited after the money was made available before the new dispensary was actually built. I thought of my anxiousness during all the months since I had known of its completion, how I had wished to return here to see it and to find to what extent it was helping to alleviate the ills of the people.

Also in the ten years that had passed since my last visit I had not been able to erase from my memory a look of a deeper suffering that I had seen in their somber eyes . . . something that spoke of more than poverty and pain. And the more I had thought of the new dispensary the more I had wondered whether the added medical help would be enough. Gradually I had become obsessed with my need to understand their needs better, and at last I had set off on my return journey.

But how was I to get to know them better, I wondered, as I watched them dance. I studied their intense faces and saw in their eyes the strange searching look I remembered. I found myself wondering if I might discover among them an especially familiar face, perhaps the old woman whom everyone called Ma, or the Moslem named Duana, the girl who had cared for my room, or an orphan boy I had met before?

I realized when I did not see any of those, or at any rate did not recognize them, how much had changed in those ten years. Everything was the same yet everything was new . . . new missionaries, a new chief, new faces. But as I watched them dance I felt a deep empathy, as one often does when returning to one's home town. Still my understanding of them was as shadowy and incomprehensible as it had been all those years.

I wondered about the meaning of their dance, and as I watched closely it seemed to me that they gave me something special of themselves. Or was it some message they sent, some mysterious message about their needs?

And that picture of the dancers was still with me much later that night as I sat with Sister Lena in her living room and listened to her account of the midwife training program. The flickering shadows of the lantern light on the wall reminded me of the dancers, and as the nurse talked I watched the shadowy movements, almost as if in a trance.

Finally Sister Lena rose to go to bed. "You must come to the dispensary in the morning," she said, "and see how I have to handle the people."

"Yes," I promised, "I will come."

Three

A RINGING BELL awakened me. I opened my eyes and sat up, startled. Bong, bong, bong, it rang again. I looked around the room. Shadows of the blinds at the window beside my bed lay like prison bars across the opposite wall. On the floor beside me the lantern still burned, its flame weak now in the dim morning light. The stuffy odor of kerosene smoke filled the room.

The bell rang again and as I sat there in a half-awake daze it seemed to beckon me from afar to rise up from the gloom that surrounded me and to seek some answer, something that would be as clear and positive as the sound of the bell.

I rubbed my eyes and remembering where I was I began to wonder why a bell would be ringing here in the middle of the jungle. I threw back the mosquito netting that draped my bed and reaching out I pulled open the aluminum blinds at the window. Beyond the trees in the distance, high and bright against a blue sky, I could see the church tower, vibrant with the sound of the ringing.

A moment later I heard, coming from across the road, the singing of a hymn. Then, as if on signal, a motor began to roar. I learned later that this was the generator, turned on early every morning so that the people at the Sanoyea mission could communicate by radio with the other Lutheran missions, their only outside contact.

Sitting there surrounded by the mingled confusion of all the sudden sounds, I thought of what had happened in the dispensary last night and I felt a deep despondency. Yet, as I listened, all the sounds of morning seemed to be filled with hope and vigor. I realized that already Sister Lena might be tending new patients in the dispensary and waiting for me to come.

I rose and while I dressed the cheerful, inspiring, yet demanding note of the church bell seemed to echo through my room.

When I went into the living room I saw the house girl standing idly by the kitchen door as if waiting for me.

"Good morning," I said. "Where is Sister Lena?"

The girl looked young, not more than a teenager, I thought. She wore a print dress with a blue border at the bottom, and on her feet simple rubber sandals. She glanced down shyly as she spoke. "Sister Lena gone to the dispensary to hold prayers."

I went to the front window and heard voices, across the way singing another hymn. "Today isn't Sunday," I said. "Why did they ring the church bell?"

"They ring it early every morning," she said.

"But why?"

She shrugged. "I guess they don't want nobody to forget about the church."

I studied her face wondering what the church might mean to her.

She glanced away, then she nodded toward the dining area. "You eat now?"

I sat down at the table where she had laid a place for me. "What is your name?" I asked.

Her eyes flashed at me. "My name, Gami."

She turned quickly then and went into the kitchen for my tea. When she came back I saw that she frowned, her face tight as if she held something pent up inside.

"Do you go to the mission church?" I asked.

"Sister Lena say I ought to go."

"But do you?"

"Yes, ma'am."

"Do you attend the mission school?" I asked.

"No, ma'am."

"Do you live in the village?"

She nodded.

She set the tea on the table and stepped back.

"Do you like to cook?" I asked.

"No, ma'am."

She stood in the middle of the room as if ready to flee into the kitchen. But her unhappy expression bothered me and I kept talking to her, trying to be friendly.

"Have you worked here long?" I asked.

She turned and looked at me. "No, ma'am."

At the window the curtains hung limp from the night of dampness. Yet the sun streamed in now making the large cement cross over the fireplace stand out like a warning.

"Do you enjoy working here?" I asked.

Gami shrugged her shoulders and turned away. But she did not go out. Instead she stopped at the table in front of the sofa and began to straighten the magazines.

I sipped my tea and sat silent for a while. I heard voices of people moving along the path outside. I watched Gami, and remembered that I had not seen her at the dance yesterday. Perhaps her immediate problem could not be eased by dancing.

Finally she turned back to me. "You like more tea?"

I nodded and she took the little pot into the kitchen. She walked slowly, hardly lifting her feet.

It seemed a long time before she returned, but when she did she glanced at me as she filled my cup, a frown on her face.

I smiled at her. "Gami," I teased, "I bet you have a nice smile."

She did not answer, but set down the teapot and stood at the window.

I wondered if she resented my coming. Perhaps I would be too much extra work for her. Yet as she stared out the window I felt that she was not thinking of me. The haunted desperate eyes seemed to stare at nothing.

Finally I asked quietly, "Is something wrong?"

She could no longer keep her feelings pent up. She turned sharply. "Sister Lena say I stole sugar, and I ain't stole no sugar."

I saw the hurt in her eyes, the hurt one feels when falsely accused.

"I'm sorry," I said. "Would you like me to speak to her about it?"

She shook her head. "Maybe it's best not." Her shoulders drooped, and hardly lifting her feet she started back to the kitchen.

When I went out the sun had soaked up most of the rain puddles and steam seemed to be rising from the dirt path. I had been anxious to see what kind of cases would appear at the morning clinic and I felt Sister Lena would be expecting me to come. Yet now I moved slowly, still thinking of Gami.

At the gate, two little girls, dressed in neat print dresses, stopped me. The taller one had sturdy arms and legs. The shorter one was petite with a lovely round face and big black eyes. She held up a bunch of flowers.

"Ma sent 'em," she said.

I remembered then that when I arrived I had not seen Ma, the old woman who ten years before had promised me that she would care for the grave of the plane victims as long as she lived. She was one of the people who had reached me, who had given me something from her heart.

I took the bouquet from the damp little hands and I noticed that some of the blooms had begun to wilt.

"I sorry," the little girl said, looking up at me, her face smooth and passive. "But we been here since long time 'fore church bell ring."

I smiled at their patience, the calmness in their eyes. The taller one spoke. "Sister Lena say you sleeping. Us got to wait."

I thanked them and asked their names.

Their eyes brightened. "I be Rose," said the small one, "and this my sister Marion. We b'long at Ma's house."

"Where is Ma?" I asked.

"She live long way."

Down the path I saw many patients forming a line in front of the dispensary. I wanted to see the work there. I wanted to see what was happening to the people. What was their need that seemed to be implied in their dance? And what had Sister Lena meant when she had said that I must come to see how she had to *handle* the people?

Yet, suddenly, I felt as if I had returned to my home . . . yes, really returned to my home in the jungle, and I wanted most of all to see Ma.

"Will you take me to Ma?"

The girls bobbed their heads, their eyes twinkling now.

We set off down the path that led through tall grass across the mission school grounds. Some of the mud classrooms were weathered and old, but I noticed their former thatch roofs had been replaced with tin. They all stood deserted.

"Is there no school today?" I asked the girls.

"It still vacation time," said Rose. "School start some day soon."

We came to the path that led alongside the old frame house where I had stayed during my last visit. The house was up the hill from where I stood but I could see the Andersons on the far side of the porch.

The girls turned down a path that led toward the grave. I had walked it many times during the days of my previous visit, trying over and over to face the reality of my husband's death and find some peace with which to rebuild my life. I followed the girls now and as we approached a tiny whitewashed hut I remembered that it was where Ma used to live, but it looked empty.

"Isn't this Ma's house?" I asked.

They shook their heads. "No more."

"Why?"

But in answer they only shook their heads again and led me on down the path. We passed two small stucco houses newly built along the row of huts for teachers. All the yards were swept clean but in some a few flowers grew. And at one home there was a stick fence tied together with vine.

On the right the old dormitory for boys had been replaced with an aluminum prefab one. On the left the playing field had grown up in weeds.

Beyond the compound the path narrowed. Water stood in the ruts left by the wheels of the Land Rover. Tall grass grew between the muddy ruts, and the bush crowded in on either side. There was no longer need for the missionaries to keep the path cleared for walking. With the Land Rover they could drive to the landing strip for the mail and supplies that the plane brought from time to time.

The older child, Marion, walked in front of me to lead the

way, and little Rose followed. At the streams we crossed rickety log bridges. The path stretched longer and more hilly than I remembered.

I stopped for a moment to rest.

"Ma live long way," Rose said apologetically, and I saw her large dark eyes examining me.

The dense bushes hung together, vines, large leaves, trees, almost as one. In the shady spots where limbs reached out, raindrops clung to the low greenery. In the sun the wet leaves glistened. No sound came from the jungle. And all about me I sensed a feeling of things heavy with dampness, somehow overburdened.

Finally the path opened onto one end of the landing strip. I stopped, and looking down the full length of it, I thought of how it was like a slender gash cut out of the jungle, just wide enough for a small plane to land.

Ten years before, the mission had no plane and during the dry season I had entered the village after three days of hard travel from the coast, which was only fifty miles away. The first day I had traveled by truck along a dirt road, the second day by jeep along a narrow path and the last day by hammock up and down a hilly jungle trail. Even now there was no road into Sanoyea, and I had been told that during this rainy season the trip through the bush was almost impossible. Eventually the little plane would return for me and I would fly out the way I had come.

But now as I lingered there, I thought again of the greater understanding of the people that I hoped to gain during this visit. Yet in that moment I felt the sudden forlornness of one who desperately seeks an answer without fully understanding the question.

Then from up ahead I heard Rose call, "We go this way please."

Now the girls and I walked on beyond the landing strip and

soon came to the new mission cemetery where a large rectangular area, outlined with stone, marked the common grave where my husband and all the other plane victims had been buried together.

"Please," I said to the little girls, "let us stop here a moment."

They stood beside me as I stared at the spot I remembered well. I saw the stone edge of the grave graced with a border plant. The red clay surface had been recently cleared of weeds and in the center the old camwood cross of former days had been replaced by a low cement structure embedded with a simple bronze plaque bearing the date of the accident and the names of all its victims. I must have stared at the name of my husband for a long time, for finally little Rose tugged gently at my sleeve. "Ma's house not so far now," she said quietly.

As I turned back to the two little girls, who looked at me with big sympathetic eyes, I realized that neither of them had been born when I visited this land before, and I wondered what understanding they might have of the grave. What had they been told about the tragedy that beset their village long ago?

They led me on into another path beyond, a very narrow path almost completely shaded from the sun. We moved over roots, twigs, and dead leaves.

We passed a large cottonwood tree, its gnarled roots reaching out like claws. At a distance I saw green sprigs of rice growing in a low cleared spot. Soon I heard voices, and I smelled smoke from a cooking fire. As we came around a curve I saw a round mud hut set back from the path beyond some rocks jutting sharply out of the ground.

Ma, a large woman in a faded yellow dress and a bright red kerchief, came forward to meet me. She moved with difficulty, but the wrinkles on her face softened into a smile.

"My friend," she said, and drew me to her bosom. "I hoped you'd come."

Under a nearby tree she had set out a chair for me, and now she pulled up a stool, made of reed and vine, for herself. Feeling hot and tired from the long walk, I sank down in the chair. I leaned back and studied the older woman.

White strands of hair showed at the edge of her red kerchief. Her eyes seemed blurred and from the way she squinted and blinked, I felt that she did not see well.

"No one told me that you were coming back to our village," she said, still smiling, "but when the children came running with the news that the people met a tall lady, with serious eyes and dark brown hair, I felt in my heart that it must be you."

"The people were very kind to greet me," I said. "I could hardly believe what was happening when I arrived."

She nodded happily.

"Just now as we passed the grave," I said, "I noticed that it is very neat. You have kept it for me just as you promised."

She shook her head. "I don't do much any more," she said. Then she added, "The clay is so hard, lots of the things I planted died during dry time. But I was just thinking other day that during this rain time I wanta plant some lilies there. My daughter Mary say if I ain't able, she'll plant them there for me."

She smiled, a gentle look on her face. "I got lilies that'll live anywhere."

I studied her face, thinking of what she had given me during my last visit. From her quiet sense of peace I had gained courage in my grief . . . courage enough to try to adapt to the variances of life, like her lilies, to live anywhere.

I remained silent for a long time and she seemed to sense that I was thinking of days gone by.

"Do you remember the day we met?" I asked.

"Yes," she said. "For many days I had sat on my porch and watched you come along the path going from the mission house to the grave."

She paused and folded her hands in her lap.

"And then one day you called to me and asked me to sit on your porch and visit," I said.

She smiled. "Yes," she said, "and you came and sat with me, like now."

"Then later," I went on, "you walked with me to the grave."

"Yes."

We were silent then, and perhaps she too was remembering when we stood that day at the grave, how she had reached out and touched my arm after a few moments. "Come, child," she had said, as if to pull me from my grief.

Now she leaned forward and touched my hand. "We have both grown older since then," she said gently.

I saw the smile in her eyes, the compliment she intended.

"And," she added in an appreciative voice, "we have the dispensary now."

"Yes," I said, trying to respond to her new mood. "Tell me what the people think of the dispensary."

"Oh," she said with a look of joy on her face, "everybody plenty proud."

She clasped her hands together with enthusiasm. "Not only the people of Sanoyea," she went on, "but all the people for long way around come here now, many walking for days from deep in the bush."

"Is this the closest dispensary for them?"

"Yes, and besides they find that Sister Lena know plenty medicine."

I thought of the roots and herbs used for native medicine that Ma showed me that day when she had pulled me away from the grave and taken me on a walk through the woods to divert me.

"Do the people use Sister Lena's medicine?" I asked. "Have they given up their own?"

She laughed. "No, they still use some they believe to be good. But more and more they find they better do like Sister Lena say."

"Does she have a crowd of patients every day?"

Ma nodded. "Sister Lena, she work very hard."

A dark cloud passed overhead, blocking out the sun. Ma sighed and glanced away. When she spoke again her voice seemed to tremble. "She work hard to save my daughter."

The old woman shook her head and finally she explained that despite all the nurse could do, the daughter had died, leaving her Marion, Rose, and their baby brother to rear.

I looked around and saw the children, those three and four others perched on the large rocks, silent and crouched, watching us with patient concentration.

"What about these other children?" I asked.

"They b'long to my other daughter, Mary," she said. "Her husband's gone and she live here with me too. We manage best we can." Despite the weariness in her eyes, she tried to smile.

I noticed the small size of the round mud hut. I wondered what the humble little home was like inside, and how all of them could live there. I could smell the damp thatch of the roof as it hung ragged at the edges. And to one side I saw a small black pot balanced on three stones over a smoldering fire.

"Why have you moved way out here, so far from the mission?" I asked.

Ma's soft smile faded. "I had palaver with the mission," she said, a frown on her face.

Sorrowfully, and in hesitant sentences she tried to explain

to me what had happened. While working for the mission at another station, she had been in charge of the school girls. One of the African teachers wanted to have the girls come to his house for "private instruction" but Ma found out what he had in mind and she refused to let the girls go. He became very angry with Ma. In revenge he made up some false charges against her and took them to the missionary. The white man was outraged and fired Ma. When she returned to Sanoyea she could no longer live on the mission compound.

Ma shook her head as she spoke, almost as if still unable to believe that it had all happened to her. "They finally found out what kinda man they had in that teacher," she said, "and now they fired him."

She went on to tell me that the chief in charge before Momo Kaine had given her permission to build a house on this new location. Either he had not known or had not cared that this land was part of the large tract leased many years before to the mission. Now Mr. Anderson, looking over the property with ideas of how the mission land might best be used, had made the discovery that she was within their boundaries.

"I think they gonna make me move," Ma said, discouraged.

The old woman, who had spent almost her whole life working for the mission as a teacher and Bible woman, was now hardly able physically to dig in her little garden, much less to pick up her few possessions and establish a new home. Her daughter Mary helped her plant rice, she told me, and her son sent money whenever he could.

"But the thing that worries me most," said Ma, her face somber and still, "is that my eyes are too bad to read my Bible any mo', and my legs are too stiff to walk to the church."

She sat quietly, her hands folded in her lap, a deep haunted look on her face.

When I left Ma's house, rain began to sprinkle. And as I

passed the grave it did not seem to matter that large drops fell on my cheeks, mingled with the tears that escaped from my eyes and ran down my face, for I felt caught up in the struggles of Ma's life. They seemed inseparable from my own, perhaps from those of all of us as we search for faith to see us through each day.

The path back stretched a very long way, yet moving slowly I kept up a steady pace despite the intermittent rain. When I reached the mission compound I remembered that Sister Lena was probably wondering why I had not appeared to see the nature of her work and how she had to handle the people. I hoped that she would not feel hurt that I had failed to come sooner. But my clothes felt drenched.

As I turned toward the house to change them, I glanced up. In the distance I saw the church tower. I thought of how its bell had rung with such cheer, inspiration and demand this morning. But now like a ghost, shadowed by a dark cloud, it hung starkly silent.

Four

I HURRIED to the house to change my wet clothes, for I still wanted to see the work in the dispensary. I rushed up the steps. But on the porch a tall man in a bright blue robe and a black corn-shuck hat waited for me.

"Remember Duana?" he asked, a big smile on his face.

"Duana . . . of course! I was looking for you in the crowd yesterday."

He stepped forward then and shook my hand. "I glad you not forget me," he said kindly.

I remembered him instantly as the man who ten years before had befriended me, yet he had startled me on our first meeting by asking *why* I had come to where my husband died. "Your husband buried here," he had said softly, "but you not find him." I was shocked that anyone would speak to me in such a bold manner. Yet there was only gentleness in his voice when he had asked, "Why you come here?" It was as if he sensed my deeper longing for a new faith, a new meaning for my life, and was trying to force me somehow to realize the true reasons for my search, a search that had led me as if I were pulled by a magnet across an ocean and a jungle to my husband's grave. I remembered that I had answered him as honestly as I could at the time, for I had not yet discovered the answers to any of the questions about life that plagued me. I had said simply, "I don't know why I have come. I just felt that I had to."

I remembered how we had sat on the porch of the old mission house for hours and talked of many things. He told me of the differences in the backgrounds of the local Kpelle tribe and his Moslem ancestors who had moved down generations before from the north of Africa. He had talked too about the changes in all their lives with the coming of the missionaries who brought their Christian message, their western culture, and a different kind of medicine. He had made me aware of the complexity of life for anyone who is drawn away from one belief yet is never quite able to replace it completely with another. Later, he had written a simple yet beautiful letter to my son asking him to come to Sanoyea when he grew up. The letter had been a plea that someone might come some day, "Not just to visit or bring Christian message but maybe to help my people learn, so they can be proud to be African."

I studied his face now as all these memories rushed forth. He seemed exactly as I remembered him. Neither had he aged nor had he lost his warm friendly spirit. His deep penetrating eyes twinkled.

"I have brought you a gift to welcome you back to Sanoyea," he said, and he held out a pan of raw meat.

"I killed a wild deer," he went on, obviously delighted that he could offer me such an important present.

"Thank you, Duana," I said, "this is very kind of you."

He smiled, his gleaming white teeth showing. He had a wide nose, thick lips, and a smooth flexible face that moved easily from one mood to another.

He took off his corn-shuck hat and held it in his hand. "All meat hard to find," he said. Then, grinning, he added, "But I lucky to kill deer when I hear you coming."

We sat in chairs on the porch. The tin roof overhead seemed like a heavy hand holding the heat and humidity around us. I forgot about the dampness of my clothes and in that heat they were soon dry.

Duana adjusted the folds of his robe and then his eyes seemed to examine me, perhaps to look into my soul as he had on my previous visit. He hesitated and then spoke directly.

"How is your son Frank?" he asked.

"You remember his name?"

"Yes, I know you say you name him for your husband, and I see his name every time I pass the grave." He glanced down sadly.

"My son has grown tall," I said, "and is very like his father."

"I picked up two fans that lay on the table beside me and passed one to him. He nodded his thanks.

"Do you pass the grave very often?" I asked.

"Yes," he said, "usually when I go into the bush to hunt, I go that way."

He shook his head. "I remember those sad days, too much."

"It has been a long time," I said.

"Yes." He sighed. "Many rain times come and go."

In the stillness, no breeze stirred, nothing moved except the large clouds that drifted slowly across the sky. He sat silent, as if thinking of the past.

"During all these years, what has happened to you?" I asked.

He blinked his big black eyes, bringing his thoughts back to the present.

"I have two wives now," he said, smiling, "and six children."

"My goodness," I said amazed.

"My young ones, they all fine," he said happily.

Then through the screen we watched a family go along the path toward the village. The man led the way and behind him the woman carried a large bundle on her head and a baby strapped to her back.

"How many of your children are of school age?" I asked Duana.

He looked uncertain. "My oldest girl, she soon be nine. My oldest boy, he 'bout seven."

"Do they go to the mission school?"

He fanned himself and shook his head. "They don't go to no school."

"That's terrible, Duana," I scolded, "Tuition at the mission school must be very low. Surely you want your children to learn to read and write."

"I'm a Moslem," he said quietly. "I don't know if I ought to send my children to a Christian mission school."

Then he sighed. "But I been thinking this year I ought to do something 'bout some learning, at least for my son."

"For *both* your children," I said. And teasingly I added, "You're lucky you aren't in my country. You'd be in trouble with the law for keeping your children out of school."

He looked surprised. "You got such harsh laws in your country?"

"Important laws," I corrected.

"I hear 'bout all sort of new hard laws 'cross the border in Guinea," he said frowning. "But surely your country not like Guinea?"

I shook my head. "Our law was voted in by the people when they realized that education was good for everybody."

He nodded his understanding. And as we talked the light on the porch grew duller when the clouds passed first one and then another in front of the sun. In the distance one broke open and spilled its store of raindrops on a small spot in the jungle. But around us the air stood still, the humidity weighing oppressive.

Duana studied me quietly for a while and finally he asked, "What you do, all this long time?"

I wiped perspiration from my neck, and settling back in my chair I tried to tell him about my life. "When I went home from here before," I said, "I thought often about this village and I realized that I wanted to know a great deal more about all of Africa. I began to read and study, and finally I went back to college to learn more about all international affairs."

"International affairs?" he asked.

"Yes," I said. "It's a study about the many nations of the world and how they do and don't get along together."

He nodded.

"I wanted to come back here to work," I went on. "But when I couldn't find a way to do that, I turned my attention to the United Nations."

As I spoke he fanned himself, yet he remained attentive to my every word. "United Nations?" he asked.

I saw from his baffled expression that he did not understand. "It is an organization," I said, "of most of the countries of the world. People from each of those lands meet together to talk about many of the problems of the world. And they try to do things to help solve some of the problems."

"They talk many times?" he asked.

"Yes," I said, "they meet in a group of beautiful buildings in New York."

"You go there to visit this place?"

"Yes," I said, "and after I had attended some of their meetings and read about their work I became very impressed by what they were trying to do."

He smiled. "I like you to tell me about you and the United Nations."

I laughed and shook my head. "I couldn't do very much, but I joined a group of volunteers who were trained to speak about the work of the organization."

"What you do then?"

"Well, we talk to groups of people who want to know about the vast work of the organization done through the General Assembly, the Councils, and the Specialized Agencies that are trying to solve certain problems and help people with such things as better health and more education."

"You learn much," he said with an approving nod, "and you do great good thing."

"No," I said. "It's impossible to keep up with everything that is going on, but it is very interesting to read the reports and talk to people about the different projects that are being carried out all over the world. Especially the ones in Africa, those always interest me."

"And you think of Sanoyea again?" he asked.

"Yes," I said. "And in a way that is one of the reasons I have come back here now."

He crossed his legs and sat forward. "How do you mean?"

I hesitated before I answered, for I was not sure how I could make him understand all my reasons for returning to Sanoyea.

"I wanted to see the memorial dispensary," I began, "but there is another reason. . . ."

He waited, watching me closely.

I clasped my hands together. "I have been traveling around Africa for almost three months now," I said. "I have come here last on my way back to New York."

His eyes widened. "You just now been traveling all about Africa?" he asked, surprised.

I nodded.

He slapped his knee. "Why?"

"Well, I. . . ." I hesitated.

"What you been doing?" he pressed.

"I have been visiting some of those United Nations projects. I have seen many of the problems in Egypt, the Sudan, Kenya, Tanganyika, South Africa, the Congo, Nigeria, and Ghana."

He shook his head, amazed.

"I have been talking about these places and what the United Nations is doing in them for years," I continued, "and now I have been seeing them for myself."

"Why you do this?" he asked.

"I think it's because of the people in Sanoyea," I said slowly. "I purposely have come here last."

He frowned, a questioning look on his face, trying to understand.

"You see," I went on, "all these years I have thought about the people here in Sanoyea, the way they looked . . . sad somehow."

He nodded. "We got plenty trouble."

"It seemed to me through the years, as I learned more about the many problems in the developing countries, that this sadness might come from a different source other than poverty and disease."

He leaned back in his chair. "What you think is the reason for this sadness?"

I sighed. "I don't know. That's what I'm trying to find out."

He was silent for a moment, studying my face.

"Did you see this kind of sadness in your travels around Africa?"

"Yes, and I had to return here to see if my memory about the people of Sanoyea was correct."

He sank down in his chair. "I think I know what you mean," he said quietly. "Sometimes even when I got enough to eat and got no sickness I feel a strange sadness deep inside."

"Why?" I asked.

He shook his head. "It hard to explain."

I waited, hoping that he might tell me more. But finally he glanced away and shook his head again as if to set the question aside. "Tell me more about this United Nations place."

"It's a fascinating place," I said, "where each delegate comes to talk about the problems in his nation. And hopefully he tries to understand the problems of all the other nations too."

"Yes," he said, "that's good."

"Yet it's really more than that," I went on. "The nations, through this organization, are creating a new feeling of the need for world unity with greater dignity for every man."

He leaned toward me. "And my country?" he asked. "Is it . . . ?"

"Oh, yes," I assured him. "Liberia is a member of the United Nations."

"Ah!" he said proudly.

I sat forward trying to explain. "We are members of our own countries," I said, pointing to him and back to myself. "And through our countries you and I are equal members of the world community."

He threw back his head, a joy spreading across his face. "Oo-oh!" . . . he exclaimed apparently delighted with this concept of a wonderful larger world in which we all have some equal share.

As I watched him I thought of what it would be like to sit on the porch of my old home in south Georgia, that had been handed down in the family from my slave-owning ancestors, and talk with Duana about equality. I recalled my hesitation, ten years before, to visit this land of black people where I feared I might be mistreated just as I knew some of his race were mistreated in my land. Yet I had come, and I had found the villagers kind and compassionate. Now I wondered again, as I had from time to time during the past ten years, whether part of my tremendous interest in Africa and struggling people everywhere had grown not only out of that experience, but also out of some deep sense of guilt inherent perhaps, and maybe built up during my childhood, which had been steeped in the traditions of the fading glory of the old South.

I thought of the complexities created by the intangible barriers erected between the blacks and the whites, the Northerners and the Southerners, the Christians and the Moslems, the Americans and the Africans, and all the other groups, races, or nationalities who often are at odds with each other.

"You and I equal?" Duana asked softly. He sat forward with a sudden intensity. Then pausing, he studied me.

A line from a poem by James Russell Lowell, which had haunted me for years, suddenly came to mind and quietly I spoke, " 'In the gain or loss of one race all the rest have equal claim.' "

He nodded a smile of understanding.

Just then Sister Lena came in. The porch door slammed behind her. The nurse glanced at Duana. "We are quite busy now, Duana," she said, her voice terse. "You'll have to come back some other time."

I looked at her astounded. But without stopping or speaking to me she crossed the porch and went on into the house.

I turned to Duana. His joy had vanished. He rose to go but for a moment he hesitated. Standing quite still he again studied my face. His silent expression did not show resentment, nor did it ask me to speak on his behalf. Rather it seemed to ask a question about the meaning of friendship, about the real equality of people, about the sincerity of one human being to another. And in that moment I recognized the same strange look of hurt that I had seen in the black brooding eyes of Gami and the soulful eyes of Ma.

I offered him my hand. "I'm sorry," I said. "I hope you'll come again soon."

With his eyes cast down then he nodded, and turning he went out and along the path toward the village. I watched his slow movement, his deliberate steps, his head hung low.

Despite the heat of the day, as I stood at the door staring after him, I felt cold.

Five

ON THE NEXT CLINIC DAY I went early to the dispensary. "Every year more patients come," Sister Lena had told me. "I used to treat about eighty each day but now the number is usually nearer one hundred thirty," she said. "And with the new dispensary I can do much more for them."

The sun blazed hot on my back as I went along the path and up the steps. I paused at the doorway of the waiting room and saw the somber faces of the patients who sat crowded together on the long wooden benches. The benches, hard and backless, stretched in narrow rows across the room. Light came from the wide window opening along the front. The shade from the roof overhang and the color of the green walls helped to make the room seem less hot.

There was hardly a sound except for the whimper of a languid baby against the shoulder of its mother, the scrape of a battered sandal against the cement floor when a frail man shifted his position, and the weak groan of an old woman who sat on the back row.

A young woman near the door wore a blue print dress pulled on over her tribal wrapper. An older woman sitting next to her wore only a bright yellow and white wrapper tied at her waist. Her flat breasts hung bare and at her neck a pair of large white beads dangled. On her lap she held a nude baby. A small boy dressed in a white kimono squirmed restlessly on the bench nearby.

All the people waited wearily for their turn to see the nurse. They glanced up at me as I came in.

"Hello," I said.

They smiled then and nodded almost in unison. I stopped to greet all those who offered me their hands and to study the shy kindly look on their faces. Their eyes followed me as I pushed through to the office.

A slight young man guarded the door. "My name Steven," he said with a wide smile. "I Sister Lena's helper."

He wore tan trousers and a brightly flowered shirt that hung loose at the waist. His black eyes danced in a finely carved ebony face.

I shook his hand.

"You like to go in office?" he asked, flinging open the door and bowing to me.

"Thank you," I said.

After the glare of the outside sun, the sudden smiles of the waiting patients, and the bright face of Steven, the office seemed dark. A large desk with a card file and boxes of medicine stood in front of the one window. In back of the desk Nurse Yunger, wearing her white uniform, sat looking glum. I greeted her but she only nodded. I felt that she identified me somehow with the authority of Sister Lena and that her feelings would never allow her to be friendly.

In front of the desk Sister Lena leaned wearily over a sick child held on the lap of its mother. As I came in she nodded to me but did not turn away from her patient. "Why did you stuff your baby with polluted water?" she asked the woman, in a voice firm and unrelenting as she repeated the question.

The woman, with high cheek bones, a flat nose, and large

sensuous lips wore her green wrapper below her breast. She stared blankly at the nurse.

Helen, the short solemn-faced helper, standing at the corner of the desk, translated the question into Kpelle. The woman shook her head and glanced down at her baby. The child, perhaps ten months old, lay back limp. Its nose was runny and its eyes looked feverish.

"Don't lie to me," said the nurse. "Your baby has pneumonia because you have forced water into its lungs.

I looked at the nurse astonished. She glanced up and motioned for me to sit in a chair beside her.

She turned back to the woman. "If you refuse to tell me the truth," she said sternly, "I cannot help you."

The woman shook her head and hugged the baby tighter against her breast. Then, ever so briefly, her eyes darted from the nurse to me and back again to the sick child. They were desperate eyes. She seemed to know the seriousness of the baby's illness. How could she go away without help?

Yet she clutched the child and mumbled something stubbornly. The nurse's eyes sparked. "Why do you waste so much of my time with your lying when we should get on with the treatment?"

The woman did not answer. She sat still, her face full of hopelessness. When the nurse kept pressing her for an answer she glanced again at me as if I were part of a conspiracy. I pushed back my chair and wanted to cry out, to ask the nurse to explain what this was all about. But the nurse folded her arms and stared at the woman.

"I have told you time and time again," she said, "that you must not stuff your baby with water."

The baby whimpered and slid down in its mother's lap. Sister Lena reached out and grasped one of the woman's breasts. She squeezed it and milk sprayed out, a drop falling on the child's head. "See," exclaimed the nurse. "You have plenty of milk. You don't need to stuff your baby with water."

The woman tossed her head indignantly, drew her green wrapper up higher around her breasts and sat the child back up in her lap.

"Don't you understand?" the nurse said sharply. "I won't help you until you tell me the truth."

Helen gripped the edge of the desk as if despite her strength she found it difficult to translate these words. But when she had, the woman sighed and dropped her head. The baby began to fret.

"Helen," the nurse said to her, "have you made the woman understand?"

I studied the woman's face and saw that life seemed gone out of her eyes. Her expression was that of a frightened animal when she glanced up. Then she put her hands to her face as if to hide some deeper shame and finally she nodded her head.

"Ah, just as I thought," the nurse exclaimed. She sat back in her chair. "You did stuff your baby with water."

The woman ducked her head and did not speak.

Then the nurse reached out and taking a glass of clear liquid from the desk, handed it to the woman.

"Here, drink this," she ordered.

The mother, her spirit completely broken now, lifted the glass to her lips.

"Wait," said the nurse, putting out her hand. "I must warn you, it is poison."

Helen translated the words slowly, a quiver in her voice. The woman scowled, leaned forward, and put the full glass back on the desk.

"Ah," said the nurse, "you won't take poison, but you give it to your baby every time you stuff him with polluted water."

She turned to me. "You see," she said, "they will protect themselves but not their children."

"But why?" I asked.

She threw up her hands. "How should I know? I tell them repeatedly but they just won't listen." She consulted the child's medical card. "This is the third time I've treated this child for illness, all caused by stuffing him with polluted water."

I looked at her incredulously. "How can you be sure?"

She slammed the card down on the desk. "I know my medicine," she said. "I have not spent years as a nurse for nothing."

"I'm sorry," I said. "I only meant . . . the mother seemed so. . . . "

But she turned her back to me. Picking up a hypodermic needle she quickly put an injection in the thigh of the baby. The tiny infant screamed, and over the noise the nurse shouted instructions to the mother. "You must stay here to care for the child until he is well," she said.

She wrote on the card and passed it to the African nurse, who until then had sat morosely studying her hands. "Here, Miss Yunger," she said, "give her these pills."

The young nurse selected carefully from two boxes, and rolling the pills in a scrap of newspaper she handed them to the mother, explaining how she must use the medicine. I studied the woman's face which seemed lifeless as she held out her hand.

Only dull sunlight came in between the opened aluminum blinds. An electric bulb hung over the desk but no light came from it. The cement floor seemed splotchy and grey. A musty odor mingled with the smell of medicine filled the air.

"Steven," Sister Lena called, and the boy who guarded the door to the waiting room came in. "Find a place out back in one of our convalescent huts for this woman and child," she said wearily.

Turning to the mother, she said, "Bring the baby back this afternoon for another shot."

Without looking at the nurse, the mother nodded, and then followed Steven through a doorway into the back hall. Although she did not glance in my direction, her distress seemed to pull at me. I rose and followed after them, out of the stuffy room.

In the hallway Steven stopped at a large closet, and scooping up some rice and cornmeal with a pan from two big burlap bags, he gave the pan to the woman. Then he led her out the side door into the yard, where clouds hung over a sultry sky.

Just beyond I saw rectangular mud houses with tin roof overhangs standing in a row across from the dispensary. In front of one a thin man sat crouched on a raffia mat, a wide white bandage around his leg. At the doorway of another a woman braided a little girl's hair. Farther down, two women leaned over a black pot that was balanced on three stones over a fire. A baby lay on a mat beside them, a large bandage on its neck. I followed on across the yard.

Steven assigned the woman a room in one of the houses. The only thing in the room was a stiff wooden cot covered with a long cloth bag which was slit open down the middle and stuffed with dry straw.

The woman laid the baby on the bed. I stood at the door for I wanted to speak to her, to find a way to comfort her. But when she turned and saw me there she frowned and closed the door. I felt stunned, as if I had betrayed her somehow. I wanted to knock on the door and beg her to help me understand.

"Are you coming?" Steven called to me as he headed back to the dispensary.

I turned away from the door, but for a moment longer I stood there under the overhang and stared out across the grounds. I watched an old man come from a little outhouse, adjusting his robe. Beside a long hut, stretched out below the crest of the hill, a man lay languid in a hammock. From an open doorway beyond I heard an old woman groaning.

All around me the yard, washed clean with the heavy rains, looked desolate. The huts stood almost bare. A deep sense of austerity seemed to hover around the patients, who appeared sick in spirit as well as body.

Silently I followed Steven back inside. Nurse Yunger still leaned wearily against the desk. Helen, waiting beside Sister Lena, stood stiffly as if numbed by repeating endless questions.

A young girl with a tribal scar on her cheek held a tiny baby on her lap. Her shoulders drooped and her eyes looked wary.

"Why have you stuffed your baby?" Sister Lena demanded.

The girl sighed.

"You know I won't help you until you admit that you stuffed your baby," persisted the nurse.

Unable to hear any more, I went through the office into the waiting room. Patients still filled the benches. A baby cried out and its mother pushed her breast into its mouth. A man sighed and put his head in his hands. An old woman coughed, bent over, and held her arms against her chest.

Steven stood at the front door. "There are no more seats," he called down the steps. "You must form a line outside."

I pushed past the couple on the steps and went down the path. At the gate to the nurse's yard, I stopped and leaned against one of the two huge cottonwood trees that framed the entry of the path. I felt myself trembling inside, and for a few moments I did not notice that a thin rain had begun to fall beyond the protection of the tree. Why must the people suffer such indignity, I wondered.

I thought of the despair on the faces of the mothers. If they did stuff their babies with polluted water, why? Why would they deliberately harm their own children? I remembered the look of innocence and then the disgust in the eyes of the woman when the nurse asked her to drink poison. There must be an answer, for obviously some basic understanding was missing. But to whom would I turn to learn more?

That night Sister Lena and I had dinner in the home of Pastor Bypou, the native minister, who lived in a neat mud house on the mission compound. Also there were two other guests, a minor government official stopping over on his way across country, and Miss Amanda Gardner, a teacher and housemother for the girls who lived at the mission school.

The meal of rice and palm nut butter, sweet potato greens and bits of chicken was served by Mrs. Bypou, an attractive, well-built woman who had received little formal education and spoke no English.

As we ate the strange food, which proved to be delicious, I listened to the minister, a short solid man with a flat nose and serious eyes, question the government official. The tall man from Monrovia spoke of the many things that should be accomplished in the "back country" and how the authorities in the capital city were talking again about finishing a road into Sanoyea. But I remembered hearing talk about that road ten years before, during my last visit!

Sister Lena, obviously weary from her long day of struggling with her patients, hardly spoke.

I turned my attention to Miss Amanda and asked her about her interests. I watched fascinated as she flashed her big eyes and spoke in a steady, almost singsong voice, telling me of her many years as a teacher at the mission school. Also there was something vivid yet quiet and humble about her as she spoke with great understanding about life in the village.

I felt instinctively that she would know the answer to why the mothers stuffed their babies with polluted water, and the next morning I went to her house.

We sat on the steps of her open porch. Her home consisted only of three rooms attached to one end of the dormitory built for the school girls who lived at the mission.

She wore a simple cotton dress with two pleats in the skirt front and had her greying hair done up in tight little knots on her head. There was hardly a line in her face but her hands, long and thin, showed the years of hard work.

As I visited with her I asked, "Have you always lived here in Sanoyea?"

She shook her head. "My great grandfather served as an early President of Liberia," she said. "My people came here originally from the Congo."

She sat quite still, a wistful look on her face. "But I have lived back country here for many years," she went on. "I have a farm up that hill." She pointed in back of her house beyond a path that led past the Anderson's old frame mission house which stood just across the way.

"And besides my farm and my teaching I have these girls to care for." She indicated the dormitory.

A small child in a sleeveless dress appeared at the door and spoke to her in Kpelle. Miss Amanda answered the child cheerfully, and when the little girl was satisfied she turned away smiling.

"About ten of the thirty girls here belong to me in one way or another," Miss Amanda said, her eyes fondly following the child.

"How do you mean?" I asked.

"Their parents are too poor to help them get an education, so I pay their school tuition and do what I can for them."

I marveled at what she told me. "How many children have you helped in that way?"

She shook her head, her large eyes bright. "I don't know," she smiled. "I lost count years ago."

Some of the smaller girls played a jumping game on the

path in front of the house, and two older girls spread out their laundry on the grass to dry. A big red-brown dog that she called Lion lay on the porch, while a small black and white mongrel called Do Yo Part sniffed around the yard. A pair of geese waddled past the steps. Two birds quarreled in a tree not far away. A palm grew nearby, its branches like green fans motionless in the still air.

I watched Miss Amanda as she talked. Her big eyes seemed to light up and then darken with emphasis as she told me about her "adopted" children.

"I'd like to know more about the village people too," I suggested.

She leaned back. "They mostly good folks," she said with a friendly laugh, "though you might think they got some strange ways." Still smiling she shook her head as if wondering just what I wanted to know.

"Is it true," I asked finally, "that the women stuff their babies with polluted water?"

The smile drained from her face and for a moment she stared at the ground. "The stream water is the only water they got."

"Yes, I know, but do they actually stuff it into their babies?"

Miss Amanda looked at me, hesitating as she shaded her eyes from the sun. "Ya-es," she said, speaking the word strangely as was her custom.

"But why?"

"It's a long story," she answered, still examining me as if to understand the reason for my interest.

"Please tell me."

"First," she said, "you got to know some of the ways of the people."

"What ways?"

"Well," she said, adjusting the pleats of her dress, "some

time the people know one thing but pretend to believe something else. And it's what they pretend to believe that counts."

I looked at her, bewildered.

"Like the way they think about babies," she went on. "A first baby 'most always dies. They don't grieve so much 'cause they know, 'most for sure it gonna die. Usually it's because of a long and hard delivery, but they believe the spirit of the ground claims the first child for itself."

She sighed. "And even the next two babies can't be claimed by the mother."

"What?" I exclaimed. "A mother doesn't claim her own child?"

She shook her head. "No," she said, "everybody gonna say those babies belong to the girl's mother."

"Why?" I asked.

She laughed at my amazement. " 'Cause it be a terrible disgrace. If the girl say, 'This my baby,' folks gonna say, 'What, what's that you say, how you get a baby, where it come from?' "

As Miss Amanda talked she threw back her head and imitated the villagers' shock over the scandal. She played the parts of two gossips talking to each other.

Then she turned back to me. "Everybody know who the baby belong to, after all they see her walking round pregnant all those months before it's born. But everybody gonna pretend it belongs to the girl's mother. Because it's easy to see that the girl is too young to know how to care for a baby."

With a nod of her head she went on. "Not 'til the girl have her fourth child can she call it her own and give it a name."

"You mean the others aren't given names?" I asked.

"Not by their real mother," she said. "Only the old lady have the right to give them names. She might talk it over with the young father, if she likes him."

"But what has this got to do with stuffing the babies with

polluted water?" I asked, suddenly fearing that Miss Amanda was avoiding the subject.

"Don't you see? The old lady gonna have complete rule over the baby. She tell the daughter what to do and the daughter got to do it. She got to nurse the baby and carry it on her back when she go to the rice field to work."

The big dog, Lion, nudged against Miss Amanda and she paused and patted his head. "When the baby gets too big for the real mother to carry it all the time, she gotta leave it home with her mama. The old woman gonna care for it the old way like she see her mama do. If the baby cry she thinks it hungry and when she feel its belly and find it soft, she know she gotta stuff it 'til the belly is hard. It only way to stop it crying. She don't have any milk, so she give it creek water."

"That dirty water!" I said.

Miss Amanda nodded her head. "Ya-es," she said, "but it looks clean and that's all they got to give the babies, and besides, they believe water is good for babies, next best thing after milk."

She sighed. "It's a sad thing to see," she said. "They'll hold a little one on their lap and scoop up water with their hand and force it into the baby 'til its belly is hard."

"The poor little thing," I said.

"Ya-es," she went on, "it crying and carrying on and getting water up its nose and in its lungs."

I thought of Sister Lena and the way she scolded the mothers. "Don't some of the women understand the damage that is done, now that they bring their children to the dispensary and hear what the nurse tells them?"

"Ya-es, some of the young mothers are beginning to wonder 'bout the old ways, but what they gonna do?"

"Why don't they take advice from the nurse?"

Miss Amanda frowned as she answered. "They don't dare

speak out against their mothers. Everybody in the village gonna hate them if they say things against the old women, 'specially if they tried to explain to Sister Lena why it is that their babies get sick again and again."

"That's tragic." I exclaimed, thinking of the way the nurse prodded them to tell the truth.

"Ya-es," she said, "but it is the custom. They must not blame their elders."

"Surely something can be done."

She shook her head doubtfully.

"What do you think should be done?" I asked.

For a long time she stared out across the mission compound. "I don't know," she said quietly.

When I returned to the nurse's house I sank down in a chair on the porch with a feeling of complete helplessness and watched two large clouds moving together in the sky. My head ached.

I leaned back but I could not rest. Instead as I stared beyond the screen I saw a woman going along the road. She carried a baby strapped to her back and a huge pail of water balanced on her head. No doubt the water had come from the stream where everyone bathed and washed their clothes. Tomorrow while she worked in the rice patch her mother would stuff some of the water into her baby and the next day she would appear at the dispensary with a sick child. Sister Lena would scold and force her to plead guilty before she agreed to help the baby. And in the days, the weeks, the months that followed the same thing would happen again and again.

I thought of the apathy, the need, the humiliation of the people. I got up and paced across the porch. I felt suffocated in the still air, the stillness before the storm. I paced back and forth, thinking of what Miss Amanda had told me.

When the nurse came in, carrying her raincoat on her arm,

I asked her directly, "Why doesn't someone teach the women how to boil water and explain to them why they should?"

She stared at me, surprised at my outburst.

"No one would deliberately hurt a baby," I said. "It's obvious that they don't understand."

"What do you mean?" she asked, her face wrinkling into a frown.

"Miss Amanda says it is a tribal custom for the grandmothers to stuff the babies," I said. "They think water is nourishing."

"Nourishing," she exclaimed, "that filthy water?"

"But it looks clean," I said, raising my hands for emphasis. "How are they to know what's in it?"

"You heard me tell them it's like poison," she said. She slung her raincoat on a chair. "They should listen to me."

I stood facing her. "It's obvious from what Miss Amanda said that they don't understand."

"And what else did Miss Amanda tell you about me?"

"We didn't talk about you," I said. "We talked about the villagers and their suffering."

"What does Miss Amanda know about it," she said. "I'm the one that has to deal with them every day."

"I realize that," I said, trying to calm my voice.

The clouds, drifting closer together, blotted out the sun.

"But after all, they are human beings," I said, "living the only way they know how."

Sister Lena shrugged her shoulders and pulled a chair away from the wall.

"Can't something more be done to help them to understand?" I asked.

Sighing deeply she sat down and for a moment seemed to study the floor. Then she shook her head.

"But why not?" I persisted.

When she glanced up her grey eyes had narrowed into a hurt look. "I *am* helping the people," she said. "If they would listen to me I could help them even more." She sat back then and folded her arms. "I'm doing all I can," she said firmly.

The clouds converged with a clap of fury and the rains pounded down.

Six

DESPITE THE HEAT, the humidity, and my weariness from a growing sense of frustration, I could not sit still the next morning. Instead, I wandered around the mission compound alone.

Perhaps Sister Lena was right; she was doing all she could. Certainly she looked tired all the time. But as I crossed the yard in back of the house I wondered what else could be done. Perhaps with some help, someone who was qualified to teach basic courses in nutrition and child care. . . .

Not far away I noticed a two-storied stone and frame building. As I approached it I could see that it was deserted. The gate to the porch sagged from a broken hinge, the screening at the windows looked rusty, and the trim needed paint. The wooden door stood open, and as I stared inside the thought came to me that perhaps with a little repair this building could be used for a training center, a place where some instruction about child care might begin.

As I stood there in the doorway I remembered my last visit to this building. When I was there before it had been the orphan's nursery, a refuge for homeless children. The mission had taken those whose mothers had died during childbirth, for otherwise, without the mother's milk, the infants were certain to die. No other milk was readily available; the tsetse fly made raising domestic animals almost impossible.

I stepped inside and in the dull light I saw cobwebs in the corners and deep shadows on the scarred walls. My footsteps left prints on the dusty floor, and I seemed to be listening for the lonely cries of the babies of the past. I remembered the rows of baby beds covered with mosquito netting, the tiny infants I had seen with Coca-Cola bottles filled with canned milk and propped in their mouths by the untrained school girls hired to care for them. I remembered the stale odor of spilled milk and wet diapers. Now there was only the odor of a damp old building left to the deterioration of time.

Where were the children? Especially I thought of one small boy, hardly ten years old, whom I had come to know and to associate with this building. I started up the stairs and somehow I half expected to find him asleep there in an upper room. For a long time I stood at the doorway of the room where I had seen him before, sleeping in the torn shirt, with its missing sleeve, that he always wore. I thought of how he had followed me along all the paths I took around the compound for many days before he explained to me his reason. He wished to protect me, he said, from any leopards that might wander out of the bush in search of ripe mangoes. Then with pride he had showed me his sling shot.

We had talked as we walked together. "You live in strong house that not leak in rain time?" he had asked.

"Yes."

"You have plenty rice that last through hungry time?"

"Yes."

He had nodded his head with satisfaction. "I hear you have man child," he went on.

"Yes." I had answered with a sigh for I was still locked in

pity for myself and my infant son who must somehow find a way to live without the help, love, and devotion of the man we had lost.

"He lucky to have mother," the little African boy had said.

I remembered how startled I had felt by that remark for it had not occurred to me that I might have something important to offer my son, for I had always leaned on my husband for direction. Then later that evening I understood better what the little boy meant when I visited the orphanage with the nurse and learned that he was a homeless child.

Now as I stared into the empty room where ten stiff cots had once stood crowded together, I thought of how he lay sleeping that night, one hand clutching the shoulder of the child next to him. I thought of what he had given me of himself, for he neither feared the leopards nor lacked the courage to approach a lonely stranger and offer a bit of human kindness.

I thought of the wisdom on his young face as we had walked and talked together. Yet while he never complained of the dreary circumstances of his life, his eyes seemed to speak to me as if to bring some message from his soul.

"Where are all the orphans?" I asked Sister Lena that day at lunch.

"They have gone," she said smiling. "That's one of the things I've changed here." She spread butter on a piece of bread. "It wasn't right to raise those children outside their own culture. Besides, it was impossible to care for them properly."

"There was a boy, about nine or ten years old," I said pensively. "I wonder what became of him."

She shook her head. "He would be . . . perhaps twenty years old by now," she said. "I'm sure he must have left here a long time ago to work in the iron mines across the country. That's where many of the young people go." She added, "either there or the Firestone rubber plantation."

She sighed. "Only a few take up religious work or remain on the mission compound to be helpful."

"That's too bad," I said. "I'm sure that the mission could use their help."

She frowned and glanced away.

"What I mean," I hurried on to say, "is that I was just thinking today how nice it would be if you had someone here to help you."

"In what way?" she asked.

"Classes for the girls and the women in basic nutrition and child care could be held in that old orphanage building that's been abandoned."

She leaned back and folded her arms. "That building isn't abandoned," she countered. "Pastor Bypou holds meetings there every few weeks for his Bible workers."

I tried a different approach. "What with all that you are trying to do for the people," I said, "I'd think that more help in health matters would be very important to you."

She looked at me strangely. "The evangelistic work is important," she said.

For a few moments neither of us spoke. Finally I asked, "What became of the small orphans when you gave up the old building?"

"I sent them back to the bush," she answered, passing me a plate of cheese and sliced meat.

"But how could they survive?" I asked, surprised.

"The family unit is very strong in a tribe," she went on. "Everyone has some relatives. I insisted that an aunt or cousin or someone take every child over two years old."

"What about the younger ones?"

She paused and smiled. "Now that I have started training midwives we don't have as many orphan babies, because fewer young mothers die."

Taking up the teapot she poured out a cup of tea for each

of us. "Of course there are many midwives who have not yet come for training, and I still have the problem of what to do with any orphans that are under two years old. They are too young to eat tribal food and without milk they will die in the jungle."

She put sugar in her cup. "I didn't like having that big nursery building so far away. It seemed more convenient to have the babies nearer to the dispensary."

She sipped her tea and went on telling me what she had done. "When I moved the babies I changed a number of things. I didn't like the old system of hiring native girls to care for the babies, because they tended to be careless and unconcerned. I found a better way."

She nodded with satisfaction and as soon as we had finished lunch she rose from the table. "Come," she said. "I'll show you."

She led me across the road, beside and then beyond the dispensary, to a mud house with a tin roof like the ones for patients I had seen along the other side. "This is the orphans' house," she said.

We went inside. The two rooms of the hut were filled with narrow cots and a few baby beds.

"When I agree to keep a baby here," Sister Lena said, "I insist that some woman from its family live here to care for it."

I looked around. "There seem to be far more cots than baby beds."

"Most of the women prefer to have the babies sleep with them," she said. "That's the tribal way. But sometimes they use the baby beds for naps for the little ones during the day."

There was no window and only a dull light came in through the open door. A sour odor hung in the air, and the mud floor was cracked and dusty.

Walking back along side of the dispensary, we came to a

mud structure open on four sides but sheltered with a tin roof attached to a pole frame. "I had this kitchen built for the nursery women," said the nurse.

In separate corners women hovered over cooking fires preparing their own rice and soup. An old playpen, no doubt left by some missionary, stood to one side, but no children played there. Two of the women carried babies on their backs as they worked. Another child, big enough to crawl, sat quietly on the dirt floor. He was gnawing something that looked like a cassava root.

"When do these women get their food?" I asked.

"Someone in their family has to bring them something to cook. That's the way all the patients manage."

I watched a woman cut up bits of potato greens and put them in a pot of water. "Doesn't that make it difficult," I asked, "when they come from a distant village?"

"I suppose so," said the nurse. "But we can't take on the job of feeding them."

We stood beside the kitchen for a moment. Sister Lena greeted the women simply by saying, "Nana, ya."

The women nodded and went on about their work. One woman sat on a stool and leaned against the mud wall. She held a baby on her lap and fed it from a baby bottle.

"What about food for the babies?" I asked.

"You'll see," she said.

We walked back to the home of the nurse, and there in the storage room off the kitchen I met Alice, a plump, attractive woman. She was busy mixing formula.

"I've taught Alice how to sterilize the bottles and prepare the feedings." said the nurse. "She comes here twice a day and makes enough for all the orphan babies."

The woman worked carefully, with obvious respect for her duties. She smiled and chatted with me as she filled the bottles. Apparently Sister Lena had devised what seemed to be a satisfactory new system for caring for the infant orphans. Things appeared well ordered and surprisingly efficient under the primitive circumstances. It was not until that afternoon that I had occasion to understand the tragedy of a single case.

While I sat with the nurse in her office as she treated her patients, an old woman came in. She was neatly dressed and had a multicolored cloth tied around her hair. On her arm she carried the tiniest baby I had ever seen. It wore only a string fastened around its waist. Its bones seemed to press through its skin, which was wrinkled and shriveling up. Yet its head was beautifully shaped, its eyes wide and expectant. In a wild ravenous way it sucked one tiny fist.

"I am a midwife," said the woman.

"Oh, yes I remember you," said the nurse. "You were in one of my classes last year."

The woman held out the baby. "I delivered this little boy three months ago."

"Three months?" I looked at it unable to believe that it was that old.

Sister Lena took the child in her arms. "Its navel is healed," she said. "Yes, it could be three months old."

The woman went on with her story. "Today, when I pass through the village of this child, I stop to see it. I find it laying on the mat, like this. I ask where its mother. They tell me she die two weeks past. Nobody feed it."

"Do you mean that this child hasn't had any food in two weeks?" I asked.

"It's father try to feed it little rice water," she said.

Sister Lena put the baby on the scales. "Just barely five pounds," she said.

She pulled the fist from the baby's mouth and I saw that the knuckles were raw from being sucked. The baby began to fret and as soon as she released its arm it immediately began to suck its fist again.

Taking up a pair of scissors the nurse cut off the dirty string from around the child's waist. "This thing is supposed to ward off evil spirits," she explained to me, "to keep the infant from harm." Frowning she threw the string into the trash.

"Helen," she called to her assistant, "give this child a bath. And tell Alice to prepare a bottle for it."

She turned and spoke to the old woman. "You must stay here and care for this child."

"No," the woman protested, "it is not my child. I cannot stay. I have brought the child's sister."

She pulled a little girl out from behind her skirt. The child was so small that in our concern for the baby we had not even noticed her. The little girl ducked her head shyly. She could not have been over six years old.

"What do you mean?" the nurse asked indignantly. "I can't put a baby in the care of a small child like that."

"I cannot stay," said the woman.

The nurse sank down in a chair. "Where is the child's father?"

"He home, long way village from here."

"Why didn't he come with the baby?" asked the nurse.

The woman shook her head.

The nurse sighed, a look of dismay on her face. "Why didn't he bring the baby right away, as soon as its mother died?"

The old woman shrugged her shoulders. "He not know what to do. I bring baby for him."

Sister Lena pressed her hands back against her hair. "We have no staff to care for babies," she said. "This child must have someone."

"I cannot stay," said the woman, and she pushed the little girl forward again.

"Don't show me that child," the nurse said impatiently. "Go and get Chief Kaine."

The woman nodded and pulling the little girl with her she went out.

The nurse looked weary. "These people expect me to do everything for them."

"At least the woman took the trouble to bring the child here," I said. "She has confidence that you will save its life."

A short time later the midwife came back. The chief was with her. He looked more western than I remembered for now he was dressed in long pants, a white shirt open at the neck, and a straw hat. "What's the trouble?" he asked as he entered the office.

Sister Lena explained what had happened and showed him the baby, who still looked frightfully pathetic despite the fact that it was clean and dressed now in a diaper and little shirt.

"You must send for its father and make him understand that a woman must come here to care for this baby," she said. "Otherwise it will die."

The chief nodded and turned to the old woman. "What is the village of this child?" he asked.

When she told him, he shook his head. "It's a long way," he said, "but I will send a runner."

The woman agreed to stay the night with the baby. And late the next morning the father arrived. He had walked since dawn. When I saw the little girl he brought with him, I felt like weeping.

"This my grownest daughter," he said.

Sister Lena stared at her. "How old is she?"

The man looked worried and overworked. "I not 'member how many rain times since her come to us."

"She can't be more than seven or eight years old," said the nurse.

"Do you think she could be ten?" I asked, hopefully.

"No," the nurse replied, blinking her eyes with dismay.

"She only other one I got," said the man. "And I need her home."

It was obvious that the man had come only on the demand of the chief and that actually he had no intention of parting with his eldest daughter, who must have assumed much of the work done formerly by his wife.

"Is the baby your only son?" asked the nurse.

The man nodded his head and studied the ground.

"Isn't it important to you to have a son?"

"Yes, Missy."

The nurse put her hands on her hips. "Then if you expect to have your son grow up you'd better be thinking of *him* right now."

The father glanced up at her. "You think my son live?"

"Possibly," said the nurse. "He will get milk here, and after two years he might be strong enough to return to life in the bush."

The man looked doubtful and he hesitated a moment longer. Then putting his hands on the shoulders of his oldest daughter he said, "I leave her with you."

The girl stood passive, her eyes large but without expression. No one seemed to care what she thought of the matter. She must do whatever she was told.

Sister Lena shook her head. "Isn't there anyone else, a grandmother, an aunt, someone older?"

"No one," said the man sadly.

The nurse looked defeated. "We'll have to see what we can do."

She led the man out to the nursery kitchen. "Perhaps these women will help the child care for your baby if you will cut some wood for them."

"I cut plenty wood," the man said agreeably. And he promised to send some rice for the little girl.

When Sister Lena explained the situation to the women they nodded. "Yes, we help."

That night I lay awake for hours. In the dark I thought of the whole tragic story, the tiny baby and his sister hardly old enough to understand what to do, the father frightened and overburdened, the other little girl overworked, probably at this very moment crying from loneliness without her mother or older sister to comfort her.

I lay there thinking of the people. Where should one begin to help them—with medicine, with education? I thought of their many ills, and how the medicine seemed almost wasted without a clean water supply. I wondered why the education offered by the mission did not include any practical help in nutrition and sanitation. Everything needed to be done at the same time. But was that possible? Was there any way that more could be accomplished? Who would care, who would try?

At the end of a week the baby had gained a pound. "Maybe there is hope," said the nurse, for the first time since the baby came.

"Let me hold the little fellow," I said, taking him up from the scales. "He is as small as a doll."

As I held him nestled in my arms his big black eyes studied me. They seemed to hold the wisdom of an old man. It was almost as if he discounted his tiny emaciated body, as if he asked no sympathy for his slim chance for survival. But his expectant gaze, steady, unblinking, penetrating, seemed to hold me, and as I studied him I thought of the little orphan boy whom I had met on my previous visit. His way of looking at me had been much the same. I realized now that the look spoke of more than the need for food, shelter, and mother love.

Perhaps a special hopelessness had been born in the children, handed down from one generation to another . . . a hopelessness that sprang from the human spirit.

I laid the baby back in his basket, and turning, I went out, but all day long I felt haunted by him.

Seven

ONE AFTERNOON when Sister Lena rose from her nap, Steven appeared at the door. "Can you come right away?" he asked. He stood on one foot and then the other, his eyes apprehensive.

"What's wrong now?" asked the nurse, as she straightened the collar of her uniform and tried to secure a loose pin in her hair.

"A mother has brought her daughter to the dispensary," he said. "And the woman gave me this message from the town chief."

Sister Lena took the note and read it aloud to me. "We are holding a man for rape. Please examine this girl and let me know if we should punish the man."

Steven, looking embarrassed, hurried back to the dispensary.

With a frown the nurse finished pinning her hair into place and went out. I went with her.

As we crossed the road I noticed her face stern with what seemed to be indignation, but she did not speak of it. I wanted to ask her about the tribal rules of morality but she seemed reluctant to discuss that matter. Instead she told me about some of the many things she was doing for the people.

She drew my attention to a woman who was hanging large lengths of cloth on wire lines strung up under the front overhang roof of the dispensary. "She is our dispensary laundry woman," she said. "And those are the mattress covers."

We went along the path. "Each time a patient leaves we burn the stuffing from the mattress and wash the cover before it is used again for the next patient."

She walked briskly and I saw that it was useless to try to discuss any other subject with her. "Do all the people have mattresses for their beds?" I asked, remembering the lumpy one I had seen that day I had followed Steven, the little woman, and her sick baby out to the recuperation huts near the dispensary.

"Some of the people in the village still sleep on raffia mats, but we furnish mattresses for all the people who stay here," she said proudly.

"With what do you stuff the mattresses?"

"Dry grass," she said. "Every time we have the lawns cut, we spread out the grass to dry in the sun. Then we store the grass to use for restuffing the mattresses."

"Are there ever any bugs or thorns in the grass?" I asked.

She shrugged her shoulders as she strode ahead. "Sometimes," she said. "But it's the best we can do."

Inside the waiting room another woman had pushed the benches back against the wall and was scrubbing the floor. "I have everything cleaned thoroughly once each week," said the nurse. "I don't know what will become of this building when I'm no longer here. I doubt if anyone will care for it properly." She sighed. "I do all I can for the people."

We went into the office. "Where is the girl?" asked the nurse.

Steven stood to one side talking with a woman in Kpelle. The woman wore a blue plaid wrapper and sandals. She stepped back revealing a child standing between them.

"This her," said Steven, his hands on the little girl's shoulders.

I looked at the child in disbelief, for she stood not three feet tall.

"How old is she?" asked the nurse.

Steven glanced down, an embarrassed look on his face. "Her mama say she only five years old."

"Imagine," exclaimed Sister Lena with disgust, "a five-year-old child being raped!"

The little girl, with a lovely round face, wore a faded red print dress. She stared at us out of solemn innocent eyes. Then reaching out shyly she grasped the skirt her mother wore. I felt that she had not the vaguest idea of what this visit to the dispensary was all about.

"Come into the examining room," said the nurse.

The child was too small to climb onto the examining table. Steven picked her up, carried her into the next room, and put her down on the table. Then discreetly he went back into the office with the mother and closed the door.

I stood at the end of the table with the nurse, who folded back the child's dress. She wore no other garments.

Sister Lena pushed her legs apart and showed me the lips of the genital canal. In the dull light from the window they looked grey edged with pink.

The nurse nodded. "This child has been molested," she said.

"How can you tell?" I asked.

"Don't you see how red this membrane is?"

I looked more closely. "It doesn't look very red to me," I said.

"It's red enough to indicate what happened," she said, and I saw a frown of distaste on her face.

I glanced back at the child. "I don't see any signs of semen," I said.

She pulled the child's dress down. "It's probably much too late to find signs of that."

"Are there no other ways you could be sure?" I asked.

For a moment longer she stood there looking at the child sympathetically. Then shaking her head she turned away. She washed her hands at the sink. "I'm as sure as I need to be."

I stood beside the table looking at the child, unable to believe what the nurse said. The little girl stared at me, her face placid as if she were removed from all that happened. Her big expressionless eyes told me nothing.

In the office Steven and the mother stood waiting. Sister Lena walked past them without speaking and went to her desk. She searched around for a piece of paper and then picking up a pen she began to write.

The woman stepped forward. Steven too seemed anxious.

"Has my little girl. . . ." the mother put out her hand. "Has she been . . . ?"

Without looking up the nurse nodded.

The woman bit her lip and stepped back. Steven shook his head and turning he went into the other room for the child.

When the little girl stood beside her mother the woman reached down and pressed her against her skirt. Yet the child seemed calm and still oblivious to what was going on.

But I noticed how agitated Steven seemed. He stood to one side, his eyes bright with alarm. "The man said that he didn't harm the girl," he said quietly. "He only touched her with his finger."

"That is not for me to decide," said the nurse.

"If you are sure," said Steven. He hesitated but the nurse did not answer. "It will mean bad punishment for the man," he went on.

Sister Lena, busy with her writing, ignored him.

"The man," said Steven, clasping his hands and staring at the floor, "is a very old man."

The woman said nothing but stood waiting for the note.

Steven glanced at the little girl, then at the nurse. "The man is very old," he repeated. "He's gone simple in the head, but I think he tell the truth when he say he only touch her with his finger."

Sister Lena did not seem to hear.

When she finished writing she turned to me. "Do you want to see what I wrote?" She passed the paper to me.

I had to read her brief report twice before I understood what it really said. Worded in stiff medical terms it was written as if for a doctor. "Surely," I said, glancing up at her stern face, "you don't expect the town chief to know what this means?"

"It is stated properly," she said, jutting out her chin. Then she glanced at the child and once again shook her head.

I stared at her, bewildered. Steven stepped forward, his hands pressed together. "I know the old man mean no harm," he said anxiously.

"Perhaps he won't receive any punishment," I said quietly, "for I doubt that the town chief will understand the report."

"The woman will tell what she believes," he said indicating the mother.

Sister Lena rose from the desk and gave the slip of paper to the woman.

Steven stood tensely, his eyes wide and with one hand pressed against his head.

I turned to him. "But Steven," I said, "if the man has molested that child, even if only by touching her with. . . ."

Steven interrupted. "The punishment much less for that than if he have her completely."

"What will be the punishment?" I asked.

"I don't know how many lashes," he said, a desolate look on his face, "but it gonna mean a bad beating for the old man."

From the window I heard a group of girls going along the road singing a hymn and in the distance the faint sound of a rooster crowing.

I looked at Steven, wondering if there could be another reason for his concern. "Do you know this man?" I asked.

He nodded.

"Is he a relative of yours?"

"No." He shook his head. "He just an old man alone in the village."

Unable to say more he turned away, went into the waiting room, and stood at the window staring out.

With sadness in her eyes, yet with a nod of satisfaction on her face, Sister Lena repeated what she had said when we came into the building. "I do all I can for the people." Then going out she crossed the road with more than her usual vigor.

I followed the woman and child down the steps and stood for a moment with them on the path. The mother frowned and seemed in a hurry. But the little girl hesitated, looking up at me with her lovely round face, innocent and passive.

And as I glanced back I saw Steven behind the screen, still staring out, as if not seeing, only searching beyond the jungle.

I did not turn toward the house. Instead I walked along slowly, thinking about the people, about injustice, about suffering. I stopped beside a narrow stream and sat down on the grass. For a long time I watched the rapid water rushing along, lashing again and again against a stone. As I studied the stone I noticed that it was worn by the relentless water, just as distress gradually wears away hope.

I thought of the cruelty, the anguish of life—how hard it is to be fair and to know what is right. And I thought too of the deep understanding that is needed for one to truly help another.

Eight

EACH DAY I tried to learn more, not only about the village people, but also about Sister Lena. I noticed how devoted she was to her work, yet I could not understand her "handling" of the people. The incongruity of this worried me and I began to wonder in what way her attitude and actions might be linked to the complex problems of the people? And I wondered to what extent the dispensary and her work there played a role in meeting their needs?

I began to join her, almost every day, as she worked. "Could I help you?" I asked.

"No," she answered, "but you are welcome to watch if you wish."

And as I watched, time and again the inconsistencies of what I observed added to my growing need to understand.

One day as I followed her out of the house I saw two children sitting on the ground near the gate. Each wore only a piece of printed fabric tied like a diaper. When they saw Sister Lena they jumped up.

She stopped. "Good morning."

"Good morning," they repeated, and they held out their hands. She felt in her pocket and gave each one a piece of hard candy. For a moment her face brightened, then it returned quickly to its usual weary expression.

From across the way near the orphans' kitchen the little girl from deep in the bush carried her tiny baby brother strapped to her back. She took a few steps toward us and then stopped shyly.

"Come on," Sister Lena beckoned to her. "Yes, you may have a candy too."

She ran to the nurse then and held out her hand.

"She is only a child," the nurse said. Then gently she turned her around so that we could see the baby who slept in the sling on her back.

"He looks stronger," I said.

"Yes," said the nurse, "he has gained another pound."

"Do you think he will live?"

"Perhaps," she said. Then addressing the little girl she added, "Maybe soon he will be too heavy for you to carry."

It was impossible to tell from the tone of her remark whether it was meant to cheer the child about the future well-being of her baby brother or whether it only indicated concern for what would become of him as he grew increasingly difficult for the little girl to handle.

I doubted that the child understood any English, but she had the candy in her mouth now so that she smiled and bobbed her head.

Sister Lena sighed. "At least the children seem to appreciate the things I do for them," she said.

"I'm sure all the people must realize the value of your work," I said.

She shook her head. "My patients don't always do as I tell them. And I've spent a lot of time training my staff, but sometimes I wonder how much they really care."

We walked on across the road. At the top of the steps of the dispensary Steven, her helper, waited. He wore grey pants and the same brightly flowered shirt, which always appeared to be neat and clean.

"Hello," he greeted us with his usual cheerful smile, and courteous bow. A slight young man of about twenty-five years, he helped out in many different ways besides tending the door. He often lifted the emergency patients, carried the sick children, assigned the ill to their cots in the rooms beyond the dispensary, doled out rice and cornmeal, and kept the card file of patients.

Sister Lena entered her office. Steven looked in the file and one by one brought her the card for each patient. He spoke to each one kindly, making sure that all received a fair turn. They sat on the wooden benches arranged in rows across the room, Steven stood at the door and called out their names and helped them into the office if they needed help.

Although the room was crowded there was hardly a sound except for the occasional whimper of a sick child. Sister Lena saw several young women with very sick babies, all of whom she insisted had been stuffed with polluted water. She saw an old woman with a fever, a man with a skin sore, a big boy with a deep cough, and a number of men, women, and children sick with malaria.

Finally, Steven called to an old man, who had sat a long time on the hard bench. The old man rose.

Sister Lena stood at her office door. She shook her head. "Steven," she asked, "why didn't you bring me this man's file card?"

"He is a new patient," said Steven. "We don't have a card for him."

The nurse looked at the man. "I remember him," she said. "I have treated him before."

Steven shook his head. "No, ma'am," he said respectfully. "This man come here one time with his sick brother."

"His brother?"

"Yes, ma'am."

"I don't remember any brother of his."

"You treat his brother," said Steven shyly, "but his brother die."

The nurse winced. "No," she said, "I have given this man medicine." Then she added, "Find his card."

Steven looked bewildered. He stood with his back to the card file, his bright flowered shirt hanging loosely from his shoulders. "No card," he said, shaking his head.

"Steven, you are lazy today," said the nurse, irritated. "Now find the man's card."

The young man stepped aside and pointed to the file cabinet. "I checked," he said. "There's no card."

The nurse turned to the tall man. "I have given you medicine before, haven't I?"

The man shook his head.

Sister Lena frowned and pushed a strand of hair from her face. "You both provoke me," she said. "I shall have to find his card myself."

The old man returned to the bench.

The nurse sat down beside the file and began to search through the cards. The sick man sat wearily, his head in his hands. Steven, trying to suppress his exasperation, folded his arms and stared out the window.

Time passed and still Sister Lena searched. "If you were more careful, Steven," she scolded, "you wouldn't lose the patients' cards."

He turned and stared at her but did not speak.

"I've told you so many times," she said, "that you must be more careful."

He turned his back and I could see the tenseness of his shoulders.

"I don't know why you can't be more careful," repeated the nurse.

Finally, she sighed and slammed shut the file drawer. "I cannot waste my whole day looking for a lost card."

She turned to Steven. "Make out a new card for the man."

Without a word Steven obeyed, and the old man rose weakly and followed her into the office.

I watched another day, when a family of four came into the dispensary together. A young man with a worried look led the way. A woman, in a blue wrapper with a baby in her arms, followed. Behind them came an old woman with strangely staring eyes.

"This my wife and baby," said the man. "And this old one, she the mother of my wife."

Sister Lena leaned back in her chair. "What's your trouble?"

"My baby, he sick plenty," said the young man. Then he stepped closer and whispered, "And the old one, she crazy."

Then pointing at the nurse he added. "I want you give medicine for baby and you keep old one here."

The nurse narrowed her eyes. "I'll decide what to do," she said, "after I have examined them."

While the young mother held the baby on her lap, Sister Lena took her stethoscope from her desk and listened to its heart and lungs. "Your child has pneumonia," she said to the father. She turned to me. "Another one that's been stuffed with water," she said with exasperation. But today she seemed too fatigued to argue with the mother.

She glanced up at the young man. "Your baby must stay here for treatment and your wife must stay here to care for the baby.'"

"Oh, no," said the man. "It's the old one I want to leave."

The nurse laughed. "People everywhere try to think of ways to get rid of their mothers-in-law. Now, you wait in the other room while I talk to her."

The old woman sat down in a chair beside the desk. She

spoke no English and Helen, the helper who was always on duty during clinic hours, tried to coax her to speak in Kpelle. But the woman seemed to ignore Helen. Instead she mumbled incoherently and her eyes wandered restlessly about the room.

"What is your trouble?" asked the nurse, trying to get her attention.

The woman put her hands wildly to her head. "My son," she wailed. "He got shot. Policeman in Monrovia killed him dead."

Then she mumbled again and waved her arms, and Helen could not understand what she said.

The nurse caught the woman's arms and tried to calm her. "Find out," she said to Helen, "what else happened."

"The spirits after me," cried the woman.

"Why are the spirits after you?" asked Helen.

The woman squinted her eyes and puffed out her mouth.

" 'Cause my husband, he burned my juju bag. I have plenty strong medicine 'til he burn my juju bag."

"Why did he burn your juju bag?"

The woman pressed her hands together. "The spirits got my son and now they gonna get me and my daughter 'cause I got no right medicine. My husband, he burned my juju bag."

She covered her face and her body trembled.

"Why did he burn your juju bag?" Helen asked again.

The woman threw up her arms. "He Christian!"

The nurse shook her head in disgust. "Tell the young man to come back in here," she said to Helen.

"I can't do anything to help your mother-in-law," she told the man. "You must take her to the mental hospital in Monrovia."

The man looked as if he had been struck. "You won't keep her here?"

"That's right," said the nurse briskly. "But Steven will find a bed out back for your wife and baby."

The man stood dumbfounded.

Sister Lena made a notation on a card and gave the baby an injection. "That will be fifty cents," she said to the father, who stood there rubbing his neck nervously.

"I got no money," he said.

"Then borrow it from your family in the village," said the nurse.

The man shook his head. "I come from 'nother village long way in bush."

"But you must know that everyone who comes to this dispensary has to pay something."

"No money," he said, deep lines on his forehead.

Sister Lena sank back in her chair. "Your child must have medicine," she said. "Will you work for the money?"

The man nodded. And after the mother had received the necessary instructions about the care of the baby, the nurse sent the family out back with Steven. As they left she reminded the man, "Come back in an hour and I'll have a job for you."

But an hour passed and the man did not return. Sister Lena sent Steven to see what had happened. "The family gone," Steven reported. "They tell me they have to go into village to get food, but I think they go home."

"Ah, just as I thought," said the nurse. "He had no intentions of paying."

Steven shook his head sadly. "I think it not possible for him to leave his wife and child."

"That's just an excuse," said the nurse. "He only wanted to get rid of his mother-in-law."

"Perhaps it was something else," I said. "Maybe he will come back."

She shrugged her shoulders. "No," she said, "the people are all spoiled. When I first came here no one wanted to pay anything." She straightened her back. "I have to be firm."

"It seems to me," I said, "that when I was here before they didn't have to pay."

"That was all wrong," she said. "The other missionaries who spoiled them didn't do them any favors that way."

She swung around in her chair. "I don't charge much. The price doesn't cover the use of a bed in the clinic huts, to say nothing of the medicine."

"I realize that," I said, sorry that my remark had disturbed her. "But because help was free for a long time it might take many years for them to understand the change."

She folded her arms together stiffly. "I give everyone who comes here anti-malaria tablets and vitamins plus all the medicines for their ills." She paused. "It should give them more self-respect to pay something."

"Yes," I agreed, "but how can they come to understand that?"

She threw up her hands and shook her head.

The next morning when I came out of the house I saw a long line of patients that extended down the steps of the dispensary and across the lawn. At the end of the line I saw the young man who the day before had lacked the money to pay.

It was past noon when Steven brought him in to see the nurse. He held out a fifty-cent piece. "Here money for baby medicine," he said.

Sister Lena took the money and dropped it into her cash box. "Where is the baby?" she asked.

"It home."

"Why did you leave yesterday," she asked, "after I had told you that your wife and baby should stay here?"

The young man stared at the floor as if unable to answer.

"Tell me," the nurse insisted. "Why did you leave?"

He clasped his hands together but did not speak.

"I told you how ill your baby is," pressed the nurse. "Why did you take it away?"

The man bit his lip but said nothing.

"Don't just stand there," said the nurse. "Tell me."

He dropped his hands. "Old one not let my wife and baby stay here."

"Why not?" the nurse asked suspiciously.

The young man shifted his weight from one foot to the other. "Ever since her son die she been strange in the head. She not let my wife out of her sight. She say something gonna happen to her daughter. We 'fraid of what the old one gonna do."

"I don't know about her," said the nurse, "but your child is very ill and it ought to be here."

The man nodded. "Soon as I get old one in hospital in Monrovia, I bring baby back."

"But will it be in time?" I asked.

The young man glanced at me, a frightened look on his face. Then he turned quickly and went out.

"Steven," I asked, "how far does that man live from Monrovia?"

"His village 'bout hundred miles by path and motor road."

"Will the baby die?" I asked.

But Sister Lena had turned to her next patient, a young mother who came in with a screaming youngster.

When she had treated the child for a stomachache, she charged the woman a dime. "There is no telling what she fed that child," said the nurse.

Next a man wearing a flowing white robe came in. He showed the nurse an angry sore on his arm. "You Moslems have your own medicines," she said with distaste. "Why don't you use some of your magic on this?"

The man shook his head.

"You sell your awful mixtures to the village people but you know better than to use them yourself."

He looked offended. "We use when we have right medicine," he said. "Every sick need special medicine."

"Your medicines make the people special sick," she mocked.

"We give to our children," he said desperately, "and we not harm our children."

"That's what you think," she snapped.

The man glanced away but did not answer.

"All right," said the nurse turning in her chair. "I'll treat your arm, but it will cost you twenty cents."

He dug down in his clothes and brought out a rag tied in a knot around a few coins. He took out two dimes and put them on the desk.

When she had treated him and he turned away she looked at me. "I guess you think it's wrong for me to charge Moslems more than I charge the other people," she said. "But they make me angry selling awful medicines and overcharging the people. Besides," she added, "most of them are traders and they have more money."

I could see that it would be useless to try to discuss this with her, for she felt convinced of her own fairness. I rose quietly and went out.

At the bottom of the steps the two little girls, whom I had seen before, waited for Sister Lena obviously in hope of more candy.

On the path I met an old man who hobbled toward the dispensary. He stopped me and wanted to shake my hand. "All the people know about you," he said shyly. "And we thank you plenty for the medicine house."

I studied his deeply lined face as I tried to explain about the development of the building. "Many people worked hard and gave much more than I did to make the dispensary possible," I said.

Then thinking of the past and the present I gestured with my hands in a sudden feeling of despair. "Yet it isn't enough," I said.

Nine

"IF SISTER LENA ASKS where I am," I said to Gami when I left the house the next morning, "tell her I have gone to see Ma."

The sun was out and if I hurried perhaps I would not get caught in a shower of rain. I went often to see Ma. Not that I liked to climb the hills and wade through the high grass along the path, but I did enjoy Ma's company and the long walk gave me time to think. My thoughts returned again and again to Sister Lena and her relationship with the people. Despite her stern attitude toward them I clung stubbornly to the idea that she had a big heart, for there were many such indications.

I thought of her fondness for the little children and the way she always carried candy in her pocket for them. I thought of her hard task of training the bush midwives and how she explained things over and over to them. Several times I had gone with her to visit her tuberculosis patients who were isolated in special huts she had built. Each time she took canned fish to them from her own cupboard to supplement whatever food their families brought. "They need every bit of strength to fight such a disease," she had said in her concerned voice.

Only yesterday I saw her give money to a child who came to her door. In explaining this action to me she had said simply, "I try to save a few dollars from my salary every month for that child's family, because I know them to be destitute."

As I walked along the muddy path that crossed the compound I thought about what a hard life the nurse led. Perhaps it had always been hard. I could understand how being in the losing nation during two World Wars might promote more bitterness than compassion. Her life in the deaconess order had been austere. As a mission nurse she faced bleakness, hard work, and endless details to be coped with alone. All day she saw hardship and pain. Not many people, I realized, could survive the heat, the humidity, the penetrating dampness, the drudgery, and the stark loneliness of the jungle without breaking down. It was no wonder that she looked pale and thin, tired all the time. I knew that every other weekend she went to Monrovia for two days, but she found little there to divert her. She worried how Nurse Yunger would manage, and she feared some emergency might arise.

I admired her dedication to her work but I wondered why she seemed to lack a natural warmth in dealing with the people. Perhaps it was necessary, in her position, not to become completely involved, for it might be that the burden of involvement in such daily privations could destroy one. I believe every person must employ from a variety of resources enough strength to survive each day. Maybe Sister Lena could carry on her tasks day after day only because she had managed to build a deep self-confidence, a belief in the rightness of her own judgment.

No doubt many people, probably including myself, could deal less well than she did with the difficulties that surrounded her. Yet caught up in the complexities of her life I could not put aside my need to try to comprehend her attitudes and actions.

I recalled that when I had asked her to explain the circumstances concerning the dispute Ma had with the mission which had proven so devastating to Ma's life, Sister Lena had shrugged her shoulders saying that it was a palaver between Ma and another missionary. "I try never to interfere in such things," she said.

As I walked I remembered Ma's compassion, her gentleness. Perhaps she could help me better to understand the nurse.

I had come to the path that ran alongside the old mission house. From the porch a voice called out to me. "Have you seen our pet?"

It was Marcia Anderson, the young missionary's wife. I stopped and looked up to where she stood.

"Come," she said, "and see Vatika. I'm about to feed him."

I felt distracted for I wished to talk to Ma about Sister Lena, but I realized suddenly that the Andersons too might help me. I had seen little of them alone, but I remembered the tension that I had felt between them and Sister Lena, and I thought now of how little I understood the reason for that tension.

I turned from the path, crossed the yard under the limbs of a big mango tree, and went up the high steps to the porch. I had visited with the young couple only a few times before in the evening when they entertained the nurse and me for dinner. Marcia was a good cook, and unlike Sister Lena, often included in her menu such local foods as wild meat stew, fried cassava, and as a special treat for me one evening, palm wine.

"Hello," Erwin greeted me from a corner of the screened

porch where he sat with a book on his lap. I sat down near the door. Across from me Marcia sat forward on a straight-backed reed chair and spooned oatmeal into the mouth of a baby chimpanzee that stood on the floor but clung to her knee. The hungry animal licked his lips after each bite.

"Vatika," she said fondly, "you are like a baby."

Erwin laughed. "But I have to put him into a big wooden box at night and nail the lid on to keep him from running away."

"With all the attention he gets, I doubt that he wants to run away," said Marcia, spooning out more oatmeal.

Then she stroked the animal's head. "You wouldn't leave me, would you Vatika?"

"What does the name Vatika mean?" I asked, wondering how I might turn the conversation to a discussion of Sister Lena.

"It's a Kpelle word," Erwin answered, as he closed his book and put it aside. "It means one who doesn't work."

"In fact," Marcia laughed, "he takes up a lot of my time."

I studied her face and saw the tenderness with which she caressed the almost human animal. "You are a nurse, aren't you?" I asked.

She nodded.

"Do you ever help Sister Lena in the dispensary?"

"Sometimes," she said, "but she doesn't really need me." She leaned back and her face became darkened by the shadow of the mango tree.

I thought of Sister Lena, distraught because she insisted on assuming the burden of every detail of her work. I thought of the endless time she spent with her patients and the midwives. Also I often found her examining something with her microscope. She planned to do a skin graft, she told me, for a man whose open sore refused to heal. Yet I thought of the need for basic instruction in nutrition and child care. And who would teach the women the necessity for boiling water?

"There seems to me a great deal that needs to be done," I said.

"Yes," Marcia agreed, "but Sister Lena has her own way of doing things." She glanced at me quickly. She was silent then, and Erwin too turned back to his book.

"Has she never asked you to help?" I pressed.

"Yes," she answered, "she sometimes asks me to assist with a delivery." She shrugged. "You see, she considers my training in the United States less adequate than hers in Germany. And it's true that I did not learn midwifery."

I sat forward on my chair. "I'd like to understand Sister Lena better," I said. "Couldn't you tell me something more about her?"

Marcia glanced at her husband and then became very busy with scraping out the last of the oatmeal. Erwin frowned but finally he spoke. "Her midwife training program is an important contribution to our mission work."

"Yes," Marcia added, "and she seems willing to repeat each detail many times in her effort to teach the women."

I waited but they seemed reluctant to say more.

"Do you think the women practice what she has taught them when they return to the bush?"

Erwin folded his arms. "I think many of them do."

"She had all her former trainees come back here recently," said Marcia, "for a week long refresher course."

"Yes," said Erwin, "that required a great deal of extra effort on her part."

"She really tries hard to see that the women learn," said Marcia. "No doubt you have seen how firm she is with them."

"Yes," I said. "I wonder about her attitude toward the people."

Marcia shrugged her shoulders, and rising, took the empty oatmeal pan into the kitchen. Vatika followed at her heels. Erwin opened his book again and then closed it. "Sister Lena is hard to understand," he said, "but I think she means well."

"I see that she does a great deal of hard work in the dispensary," I said. "I believe she is dedicated to helping the people."

"Yes," he said, but he stared out beyond the screen, as if he searched for something in the distant jungle. "It's hard for any of us to know how to reach the people," he said, "so how can we know the best way to help them?"

When I left the Andersons I went down the path toward Ma's house. As I walked along I thought of the Andersons and Sister Lena. Each of them had come a long distance and from basically different cultures. Yet they, confined to this remote mission post, seemed to be trying to understand each other. Certainly they lived under many difficult circumstances in order to serve the African people. Erwin had been assigned the task of learning the language before he could take up his duties. The nurse had stated that she too wished to learn the local Kpelle language but she did not have the time. But what about Marcia? Was there no way she could be of more help to the people? She seemed kind and gentle and I felt that she must have both the understanding and the training to teach them ways to improve their lives.

Yet I wondered about her hesitancy to do more. Was it apathy or lack of interest on her part? Or was it because she respected the authority of Sister Lena and felt that to argue with her over the way the people might best be helped would only lead to more tension and confusion? I remembered something Duana had said to me on my first visit years before. "When the missionaries come here and tell the people that their way is all wrong, then the missionaries disagree among themselves, the people don't know what to believe."

I remembered the old adage: You can't please everyone and expect to offend no one. There was so much to be done, and it seemed to me that it was the Africans who were being hurt most by the confusion and lack of more positive action.

Yet it was hardly fair to expect more from any missionaries when spreading their religion was no doubt an arduous and full-time duty, their real reason for being there. Still, at the moment it seemed that even though the Andersons might have greater empathy with the people, it was Sister Lena who worked hardest on their behalf.

I knew it was unfair for me to judge any of them, for the villagers, the Andersons, and Sister Lena were all living and working in the best way they knew how. After all, each of us is nothing more than a product of our own experience. And each of us must find our own way to live in whatever way we can. For some, opportunities seem to open like doors. For others, barriers seem to grow up no matter which way they turn. Lucky ones are spurred on by success, others fall victim to constant defeat. Is it true that the real worth of a man is measured by the courage he finds with which to face adversity? Or does daily unrelenting hardship spear to death one's courage and perhaps even one's understanding of what one needs and what one has to give?

I walked along the path slowly, thinking of all these things, hardly aware of the mud puddles I stepped over or the stillness of the jungle growth breathing its dank heat from either side of me. At a wide stream I had to turn my attention to balancing my way across on a single log. When I glanced up I saw someone coming toward me from around the curve ahead. It was Miss Amanda and she carried a flat basket of sweet potato greens on her head. She smiled and stopped to talk.

As we stood there in the sun, finally I was able to say what I had on my mind. "You know I'm interested in learning more about the local people," I began, "but also I wish to understand the missionaries."

She glanced down as if hesitant to speak.

"Could you tell me how the people here feel about them?"

Cautiously she looked at me. "Through the years some good things have happened."

She wrinkled her brow as she spoke. "Teachers and Bible workers have been trained and now ministers, like Pastor Bypou, also try to help the people."

She held herself erect as she talked, still balancing the basket of greens on her head. "There are nurses and clinic helpers," she said, "and every year there are more children in school."

"What about the three missionaries in Sanoyea?" I asked. "How do the people feel about them?"

She studied the ground a long time before she answered. "I don't know if all the people agree," she said, "but I think the Andersons have some good ideas about helping the people. Maybe they don't always think like Sister Lena but. . . ." She paused and took the basket of greens from her head and held it for a moment in her arms before she continued. "Sister Lena, though she often seems. . . ." She paused again as if trying hard to select the right word. " . . . she often seems sad, still she does much for the people . . . in her own way."

She shook her head and seemed to ponder her thoughts. "Many different missionaries have come here in the years gone by," she said. "Some of them been plenty good."

When Miss Amanda lifted the basket back to her head and

started on her way I noticed the evasive look in her eyes. I felt that she wished to be fair, but her long years of loyalty to the mission prevented her from telling me more.

As I walked on I thought of the sadness that seemed to dwell with the village people and with the nurse. Did it stem somehow from a similar defeat within the human heart?

After I reached Ma's house I sat under the shade of a tree and talked with her. I wanted to know her feelings about the nurse, but she shook her head. "Sister Lena do all she can to save my daughter," she said. "But my daughter she die anyway."

She was silent for a moment and then as if not wishing to discuss the nurse she called my attention to the song of a bird from deep in the bush. As we listened she smiled, and then when the bird flew away she tried to find other cheerful things to distract me.

Finally when I turned the conversation to the plight of the people she sighed and shook her head again. I asked her then what she considered *her* most difficult problem.

She folded her hands in her lap and stared down at them for a moment. I noticed how thin and wrinkled they were and I wondered about her many hardships.

"It my eyes," she said sadly. "I think I'm going blind."

"Have you asked Sister Lena to examine them?"

"No," she said. "My leg too lame to walk to the dispensary, and I ain't got nobody to carry me. My daughter, Mary, she only one to help me plant rice. My son, he live long way from here."

"Perhaps the nurse will come out here to see about you," I suggested.

She looked doubtful. "I don't know if she'll do that."

Ma and I sat there in the shade for a long time and talked of many things. I asked her about the young girl who had cared for my room when I visited Sanoyea ten years before, and I learned that she had married a man who lived in a town many miles across the country. Also Ma spoke of some of the other young people I had met and how they had grown up and gone on to follow new paths in their lives. She told me about her own son and other young men who had left the village to work in the iron mines in the hills far away, and how some of them never come back because, with money, they try to find a better life in the city.

We talked about the changes that come into every life, some bad, some good. She said that no matter what else happened the pepper bird still came early every morning to wake the people so that they did not sleep too long and become lazy. She mentioned her hope that her grandchildren would have more than she had been able to provide for her own children. She wanted an education for each of them, if only she could find a way to pay the small tuition at the mission school. There was no complaint in her voice, but once again she told me how much she missed being able to read her Bible.

Though I was reluctant to leave the calmness, the quiet wisdom I felt in her presence, I finally rose to go. She gave me a pale pink flower and sent me away with a smile.

When I got back to the compound, a heavy rain began to fall. Sister Lena came in from the dispensary looking exhausted. Rain drops streaked her hair.

I sat down with her. "I'm worried about Ma," I said almost immediately.

Sister Lena pushed her raincoat aside and sank down in her chair. "What's wrong with her now?"

"Something is wrong with her eyes."

"What's wrong with them?" she asked.

"I don't know," I said, "but she thinks she's going blind."

The nurse shook her head. "I doubt if it's that serious."

The rain lashed down on the tin roof and a heavy damp odor filled the room.

"I wonder," I said hesitatingly, "if some day when you aren't too busy, if you would walk out to Ma's house and see about her eyes?"

She put her head back against her chair. "I don't go to patients," she said wearily. "If they are too sick to walk, someone can bring them in a hammock to me."

"Ma's leg is lame," I said, "and she doesn't have anyone who can bring her in a hammock."

She sighed and for a moment closed her eyes. "Her son's no good," she said. "He doesn't help her out the way he should."

"I don't know about that," I said. "But he lives a long way from here."

When she did not answer I soon lost hope of continuing the discussion, for the sound of the rain dominated the room as it beat down unmercifully on the roof.

"All right," she said suddenly, pushing up out of her chair. "I'll go and see about Ma's eyes." She reached for her raincoat.

"I didn't mean right now," I countered. "You are tired and besides it's raining hard outside."

She stood tall, her hands on her hips. "If you are afraid of a little rain," she said, "you don't have to come."

I looked at her astounded. "I'm not afraid," I said.

As we put on our raincoats and hats and went outside I wondered if such ambiguity on the part of Sister Lena reflected the reason that the Andersons seemed reluctant to cross her. I realized that I was reacting to her, perhaps in the same way they did.

From both ends of the drain which stretched across the porch roof water poured down like two open faucets. The rain barrels were already full and the water splashed out and ran in streams through the yard.

I followed Sister Lena across the compound, continually wiping the rain from my face in order to see where I was going. Mud oozed up over our shoes and the tall grass struck our legs. On the hills we stumbled up and slid down the slippery inclines. The humidity felt like a hand pushing us back. At the streams we clung together trying to cross the wet uneven logs. No sound came from the jungle except distant thunder that rumbled like an angry animal.

By the time we arrived at Ma's house the rain had slowed to a drizzle. The old woman came out and sat with us on a low wall extending beyond the edge of her hut. The ragged thatch overhang helped to protect us from the raindrops. I took off my dripping coat and found that my clothes were wet from perspiration.

Grey clouds lingered in the sky blocking out the sun. In the dull light the nurse leaned over Ma and peered into her eyes.

"I'm not an eye doctor," said the nurse, "but I think she needs glasses."

"You don't think she will need an operation?" I asked.

"I don't think so," said the nurse.

"I was afraid it might be a cataract," I said.

"I don't see much," said Ma, blinking her eyes.

Sister Lena turned to me. "She ought to go to the eye clinic in Monrovia. The doctor there is a specialist and he will know what to do."

"How can we get her to Monrovia?" I asked.

The nurse thought for a moment. "She could go with me the next time I fly down for a weekend." Then she added, "I'll take her to the clinic if you will pay the costs."

I agreed and Ma was overjoyed. "I thank you plenty, plenty," she said throwing up her hands.

Sister Lena explained the details of how they would arrange the trip, and when we left Ma's face glowed and her weak eyes filled with happy tears.

We trudged back through the drizzle, up and down the hills, across the log bridges, and through the mud. Yet Sister Lena did not speak until we entered her house.

"I hope you realize now," she said, taking off her raincoat, "how much I love the people."

Without waiting for me to answer she went into her bedroom and closed the door.

Ten

ONE AFTERNOON I noticed that Gami's face still looked glum. "Sister Lena keep saying I stole sugar," she confided, "and I ain't stole no sugar."

I wanted to speak to the nurse about Gami but I felt that my remarks probably would be resented. Yet as I talked with the girl I realized that part of her problem was the fact that Sister Lena found her rather inadequate in her duties. I had noticed that each time the nurse invited the Andersons for dinner she had asked Helen to come to help cook. Helen had served as her house girl before she had trained her as a dispensary helper. Gami did what she could with her limited experience, but Sister Lena had no time to teach her more.

"Gami," I said to the young girl now, "would you like to learn to bake a cake?"

Her face brightened. "Oh, yes, ma'am."

She brought a recipe book from the kitchen and we sat together on the sofa. Looking through the book we finally decided to make a banana loaf.

When the nurse came in from the dispensary I told her my plan. "All right," she agreed, "if you are so anxious to do something perhaps you can make yourself useful by teaching Gami how to bake."

I did not ask her for the key to her storage closet. Instead I suggested that she measure out the exact amount of the sugar and flour that we needed and then relock the closet.

When Gami and I were ready to begin we discovered that there were no bananas in the house. "We get some in the village," said Gami, taking up a pan in which to fetch them. I went with her.

The sun was brilliant in a cloudless sky with a brightness that seemed to dance on the roof tops and on the big damp leaves of the palm trees and the cassava bushes. After we passed the church we noticed a tall banana bush in the edge of the woods. We stopped and looked up at the stalk of bananas that hung down, but they were small and green.

We went on, stopping at almost every hut to ask if anyone had ripe fruit to sell.

"Bananas finished," an old woman told us with a wave of her hand.

At one house when no one answered our call we went around back and found the young wife washing clothes in a tin tub while her baby slept strapped to her back. "Sorry," she said shyly, and she followed us back around the house as we left, still apologetic.

A woman with bare dangling breasts held out a flat basket in which she was winnowing rice. She tossed the grains into the air and caught them again and again. As we approached her she paused.

"No bananas," she answered Gami's question. "But wait." She put down the rice, and running to the side of her house she returned with a huge papaya.

I tried to explain to her that I lacked courage to try to substitute any other fruit in a banana loaf. She grinned at me, a wide grin with a missing front tooth. "Papaya good to eat," she said.

I declined her offer of the fruit as a gift because Gami whispered to me that the woman was very poor and all food for her was scarce.

At the village store we found only a few fresh papayas, a barrel of rice and one of ground nuts, a box of canned milk, some cans of spiced ham, and lined up across one shelf some bottles of Coca-Cola and the orange drink Fanta. Stacked to one side were a few bolts of cheap printed fabric. But no bananas.

Hanging from the rafters and around the frame of the wide front opening, bits of skin, bones, dried animal organs, and other indistinguishable juju medicine fascinated me. But Gami pushed on. "Come," she called to me. "We must find bananas."

The other general store had been out of bananas for several days, we learned from a flat-nosed man with wiry hair who stood in front with his arms folded.

We stopped to chat with the village tailor who sat at the front window of his mud hut pedaling his sewing machine. "Sorry no bananas," he said with a bright smile. "I too busy lately to go to jungle to look for fruit."

We walked the full length of the wide main street, stepping over puddles and trying to avoid the worst muddy spots. We passed the big red calla lily I had seen before, still bright and beautiful in its drab surroundings. I paused to touch it and make sure it was real. "There is hope," I said to Gami.

But she shook her head. "I think there not one ripe banana in whole village," she said pensively.

Finally we turned back. Gami walked slowly now. A gloomy mood seemed once more to have settled on her. She did not speak until just before we reached the far side of the village nearest to the mission compound.

"I got no bananas at my house," she said, "but you like to see my house?"

"Yes," I said, "I'd like that very much."

I wondered now if in her silence she had been deliberating

as to whether she should take a chance of exposing more of her life to me.

"You'll meet my Mama," she added shyly.

I followed her as she turned off the main street. We went around several small huts, passed the tall bush with the green bananas we had seen before, and went down a slight incline. There on a little porch covered by the thatch overhang of the round roof, an old woman squatted beside a black pot placed on three stones over a fire. She stood up when we approached and timidly offered me a limp hand to shake. Her face was worn, her skin dry and wrinkled. She wore a faded wrapper that hung from her waist almost to her knees. She looked at me with big eyes staring from an expressionless face.

A delicious aroma came from the pot, and I sat down on the edge of the clay porch and asked her what she was cooking.

"Greens soup," she answered.

I peered into the pot and saw greens, tomatoes, and onion simmering together. Tied to the end of a raffia string suspended from the rafters of the porch roof, a fish hung over the pot drying in the smoke from the fire. All around the house the yard was swept clean and only bits of wood and a few cooking utensils cluttered the tiny porch.

Two girls and a boy came from the side yard and Gami introduced them as her own.

"Surely you can't mean that you are the mother of these children," I said.

She hesitated, but her mother was busy stirring the soup, so she nodded to me.

"But I thought you were only a . . . teenager yourself," I exclaimed. Then I remembered what Miss Amanda had told me of the dominance older women exercised over their children and grandchildren.

Gami looked a bit embarrassed. "I older than you think,"

she said. Her eyes flashed down and as I watched her, I wondered about her life, her husband. Had he abandoned her? Was she supporting her family and her old mother on the small salary the nurse paid her?

"You like to come in?" she asked.

I followed her inside and across a large room furnished with a few reed chairs set on woven raffia mats which were spread out on the clay floor. Two doors on the left led to smaller rooms. She opened one of these and stepped inside a tiny bedroom. "This my room," she said, as she crossed the floor and flung open the wooden shutter letting light come in the little square window.

The blue flowered curtains that hung on either side of the window matched the cover on the bed. The only other thing in the room was a small wooden box pushed under the edge of her bed.

"I keep everything in my box," she said. I thought for a moment that she was explaining the austerity of the room or perhaps letting me know how few were her possessions. But then she added, "The ants and rats eat everything not in box."

I wished she would open the box for I wanted to know what kind of things she might treasure. I knew she had very few clothes because she had worn the same dress almost every day since I arrived, yet I wondered now how she managed always to look neat and clean.

But she did not open the box. Instead she closed the window and led me back through the house. On the porch I said good-by to the children and Gami's mother. And this time I remembered to try to click fingers in the Kpelle style of handshake that I had learned ten years before, where two people snap their middle fingers together. The old woman smiled at me in my clumsy effort and then asked if I would like a cup of soup.

I thanked her but refused, and Gami told her of our plan to

bake a cake. "You know where we find bananas?" she asked her mother.

The old woman shook her head. "Bananas much scarce now."

When we returned to the mission compound Gami suggested that we try to borrow some from the Andersons. Much to our delight we found that Marcia had bought a bunch from a trader who had passed by her house the day before. She loaned us the three we needed and Gami and I set to work.

When I opened the can of baking powder that I found on a shelf in the kitchen, I discovered that it was hard and dry. "How long has this been here?" I asked.

"Long time I think," said Gami. "I not know what it is so I never use."

"Perhaps it will do," I said, digging out some with a spoon.

Besides the sink with its single cold water faucet, the kitchen walls held a few shelves lined with the dishes, glasses, salt and pepper, a few spices, the old baking powder, bits of string, stubby pencils, and odds and ends accumulated over the years. Also there was a stove and a refrigerator, both run by bottled gas. Gami had never used the oven, but after some difficulty we discovered how it worked and finally succeeded in lighting the flame. Then we finished mixing the cake and poured it into a loaf pan.

While waiting for it to bake we sat together in the living room and looked at some old magazines. Gami wanted me to explain to her about some of the gadgets in the advertisements, and she wanted to know if many people actually lived in houses like the ones in the magazines. On one page there was a picture of a woman playing tennis and a man sailing. I thought of the drabness of Gami's life.

"What do you like to do?" I asked.

She frowned. "What you mean, like?"

"You know, things that make you happy?"

Sighing, she studied her hands which were folded in her lap. "I live one day, then the next," she said. "I not think about like."

I considered her somber face. Does an apathetic person actually suffer, I wondered? I remembered something a friend once said to me. "One cannot miss what one has not had." Yet it seemed to me that something inherent in the nature of man urges him to seek some greater satisfaction. Does not everyone feel a restlessness that keeps life moving on, some feeling of quest that prevents life from being only an existence?

Does apathy breed apathy, I wondered? Or does the urge for some meaningful individual expression lie dormant, waiting like a hungry leopard for a chance to spring forward and claim something for itself? What kind of experience is necessary to motivate one to care?

Certainly Gami had responded to my offer to help her learn to do a new thing for herself. Even now as I watched her she glanced up, a brighter mood beginning to show through. "You think our cake done?" she asked.

When we opened the oven Gami spoke cheerfully. "It nice and brown," she said. But when she lifted it out I felt like weeping, for it had not risen at all. With a knife I tried to cut it but it was like a large brick.

Later when Sister Lena came in I told her what happened. "I'm sorry," I said, "but I think the baking powder was too old."

She pressed her thumb against the hard crust. "One usually fails," she sniffed, "when one tries to show off."

Turning she left us standing there over our failure. For a moment I felt as if I had been struck.

Gami glared after the nurse. "She got no right to talk that way," she said.

Then suddenly the irony of the nurse's remark seemed to reach me. In my desperate concern for the people, yet in my obvious inadequacy to do anything significant to help them, I had tried to do a very small thing. Why? Was it an expression of frustration on my part because I did not know what should or could be done to lift the spirits of the people? Had either Gami or I learned anything from our "failure"? Something perhaps about caring, about sharing even in a small effort. Or had I been showing off?

I began to laugh, and the absurdity, the irony of it all seemed to grow. As I laughed Gami stared at me. Then suddenly all the tension of her old pent-up grief gave way, and for the first time I saw her smile, then break into a giggle.

Together we stood there in the kitchen, our hands on each others' shoulders, and we laughed and laughed until tears ran down our cheeks.

Eleven

ONE DAY I walked into the village alone. As I passed the church I saw the old cemetery, the one too filled at the time of the accident to offer space for the plane victims. I stopped to look at the mounds of dirt indicating the graves of Christian natives and at the markers put up for the missionaries who had given their lives in service here.

As I stood staring at the weathered markers I wondered about the reasons for human involvement. What makes a missionary wish to proselytize? What makes a pagan become a convert? What are the forces that control man's mind and heart, that lead him toward diversity or unity?

The hot sun pierced my back. A green bush, with pockets of water from last night's rain still caught in its curved stems, drooped over the edge of the cemetery near me, and on one large leaf two insects seemed to stare at each other. The church, with paint peeling from around its window frames, looked forlorn and deserted.

I thought of the many different religions to which man ascribes, and how each believer likes to think of his own religion as the only true one. I wondered about the ways that the religion, brought to the jungle by the missionaries such as the

Andersons and Sister Lena, must differ from the basic beliefs of the people. Yet it had been accepted by those such as Pastor Bypou and passed on to many others. What is the final test as to whether a certain religion is right for one, I wondered? Must it offer more than just a way to accept life? Should it perhaps help one achieve something more—contentment, a sense of well being, an equal place in the human family?

I noticed the tangled weeds that spread across the cemetery. It seemed as if they were trying to claim the graves of the missionaries and of the natives as one. Is it only in death that we are united, I wondered? Until then must each of us struggle alone? Feeling bewildered I turned away from the church.

As I entered the village I noticed a new house under construction. I paused beside it to watch the workmen. Poles tied together formed the frame for the sides, the roof, and the partitions of a fairly large rectangular house much more western in style than most of the village huts. The tin roof, already in place, glared in the sun, but the house stood under it like a labyrinth of lattice work, the poles varying in size. Two men fitted a wooden shutter into a window opening. And a worker inside scraped the hard clay, leveling the dirt floor.

A short man, cheerful in a brightly flowered shirt, walked over to me. "How you like my house?" he asked.

"Oh," I said, surprised to meet the owner, "it's going to be quite nice."

He smiled. "Yes, it take much work," he said proudly, "but it gonna be the kind of house I need now."

I looked at him wondering what he meant. "Will you put mud for the outside walls?" I asked.

He nodded.

"That should be interesting to watch."

He laughed at my interest in something so commonplace to him.

"I don't believe we have met," I said, trying to place him among my memories of ten years before.

"I was away short time when you visit our village before," he said.

He stood with one hand against his greying hair. "I'm Peter Giddings," he went on. "I was the Paramount Chief here then."

I remembered hearing his name and I thought of what some of the people had told me about his warnings at the time of the plane accident, that the evil spirits which caused the plane to fall would harm everyone who touched the bodies of the dead. Yet I remembered also that there had been implications that the chief might have been involved in the fact that when the white missionaries who were in Sanoyea at the time arrived at the tragic scene after the chief and some of his men, no money or jewelry had been found in the wreckage. I had wanted to meet this man before, to try to decide for myself what kind of person he really was. Yet I remembered feeling that there was something strange about the fact that he had been "away" during my entire visit.

I studied him now.

"I was chief for sixteen years," he said, glancing away shyly.

"What happened?" I asked. "Why aren't you still the chief?"

"The people put me down," he said sadly, "over a money palaver."

"I don't understand."

He frowned. "They say I keep too much tax money."

"You had to collect the taxes?"

"Yes, and part the money due me," he answered. "But they say I keep too much."

"Were they right?" I asked.

He threw back his head and laughed. "It was a scheme," he said, "of my cousin's. He want to be chief hisself."

"You mean Chief Kaine did this to you?"

"No, Chief Kaine a good man. It was another cousin who is a greedy man and the people put him down after only one year."

He explained to me that a Paramount Chief is picked by the tribal people from within the chiefdom family. It is usually the eldest son of the chief who last ruled, but not necessarily. A man might be elected for life if he serves well, but if he is suspected of any evil ways he can be put down at anytime.

"Then you were chief here when the plane fell," I said pointedly.

"Yes." His eyes flashed and I felt that he had not forgotten a single detail of that tragic day.

I thought again of what I had learned in the village before, about how frightened the people were that they too might be attacked by the evil spirits they believed had caused the plane to fall, of the fear they must have felt as they moved the bodies of the plane victims down the rugged hill to the mission for burial.

Yet now as I stood there in sight of the mission church talking to this man so western in manner, it seemed impossible to believe that such a pagan idea ever existed or that he might have been associated with such superstition.

"Did the people really believe that evil spirits caused the plane to fall?" I asked him now. "Is it true that they were frightened?"

"Yes," he said slowly, "I remember the fear of my people that day and for many days after."

He folded his arms and sighed. "When they bring the bodies down from the hill," he went on, "they take them to the old log dispensary to put them in empty rice boxes."

He paused, frowning as he remembered. "The people think evil spirits stay in dispensary. Many weeks pass 'fore anyone go again to dispensary, no matter how sick."

"I'm sorry," I said.

He shook his head and then glanced at me as if with a question on his face, almost as if he expected me to ask him to explain the action of the people or perhaps to ask directly about the disappearance of the money and jewelry from the scene of the wreckage.

As I stared at him I wanted to ask these questions, yet there was something in his manner that put me off and I did not speak.

"It's been a long time," he said, "and a few things have changed." And at that moment I felt that he was rather embarrassed by the memory of it all.

We turned our attention back to the workers and the new house, but for a few moments neither of us said anything.

"Have many things really changed in the lives of the villagers?" I asked at last.

"Not so many," he admitted, "except. . . ." He hesitated and glanced away. "I have changed," he said quietly.

I watched him and waited for an explanation, but he gave none. Finally I asked, "You mean not being chief anymore?"

"No," he said, "I change another way." He looked up as if watching a big white cloud that passed over us, or perhaps as if searching for heaven.

"How?" I asked.

He turned his black eyes to me then and studied my face, sizing me up, trying to decide how much he was willing to tell me. Just then a workman called to him from the side of the house. He bowed to me and went to help the man.

I waited and when he returned he had made up his mind. "Another day," he said with confidence, "we will talk."

The next day it rained all day and into the night, but the following morning Gami brought a note to my room.

"Man leave this for you," she said.

I unfolded the little scrap of paper and read,

> Dear Stranger Lady,
>
> Today I daub my house with mud.
>
> If you wish to see, please come.
>
> Your friend,
>
> Peter Giddings
>
> P.S. I send a chicken for your dinner.

"A chicken?" I looked at Gami.

"Yes, ma'am," she answered. "Man bring chicken too."

I dressed quickly and went into the village. The sun sparkled and the air smelled clean from the rain. The cross on the top of the mission church stood out boldly as if stamped in the center of a cloud passing behind it. The wet thatch of the village huts glistened and curled in the drying warmth of the morning.

As I approached the new house I could see that the daubing had already begun. Mr. Giddings, in khaki pants and his colorful shirt, stood in front, waiting for me.

"It's a fine day," he said, by way of greeting.

Workmen swarmed about the red mud like an army of black ants. Balanced on one foot, a drummer leaned against the house next door, beating out a spirited rhythm with his hands. A dozen big boys danced up and down mixing the mud with their feet.

With shovels two men on the edge of the tramping circle loosened more of the red earth. A boy standing nearby lowered a bucket of water he had balanced on his head and poured some of it on the clay. As soon as it was soft enough the dancing boys would scoop up a double handful and carry it to one of the men working next to the pole frame of the house. There were two of these men, each having begun his work at a corner of the pole structure. When they received the lump of mud they would sling their arms back like a baseball player at bat, and then slam the mud against the framework. Then with both hands they smoothed it out. The most important thing seemed to be the consistency of the mud. If it was too dry it refused to stick and if it was too wet it would drain down to the ground.

Buckets of water stood in a row at one side of the house, and a small boy bringing still another potful from the stream came down the path. Everyone except Mr. Giddings was streaked with mud. One boy dancing in the mixture sang out to me in Kpelle and carried a ball of mud on his head to make everyone laugh.

No matter what task each one did, every movement within the group seemed to be to the rhythm of the drum. "The drummer cost me more than the worker," said Peter, "but he most important man to have on job like this."

The men worked fast, and while I watched the front and one side of the house became mud walls. Mr. Giddings, apparently pleased with his work crew, gave them few instructions. Standing in the sun he chatted with me, explaining that when the daubing was completed outside, the whole process would be repeated inside.

"Just like a man," he said. "It got to get strength many ways."

Then he went on to tell me that after a few days of drying in the sun, the cracks would be filled in and once more the whole job would be smoothed out again.

"If a house is daubed again before it cracks too much, it last long time," Mr. Giddings said, and he spoke slowly as one does when repeating a parable. Yet there was sadness in his tone, a sadness mingled with wisdom.

I looked at him trying to understand his meaning. The

drummer seemed to beat louder now and he started a chant. This was taken up by the boys dancing in the mud. And the tall boy who carried a red dirt ball on his head laughed and shouted again and again, as streaks of dirty water ran down his face.

It was difficult to converse over the noise, so that I shouted to Mr. Giddings, "Surely yours will be a strong house."

He smiled but he shook his head and I could not be sure whether he heard me.

He seemed to stare at the ground for a long time and finally he turned back to me and put out his hand for emphasis as he spoke. "Some other day," he said, "we talk."

I was disappointed. I had hoped that today he planned to tell me more about himself and the mystery of how he had changed. Strangely, I felt that he had told me something, yet I could not be sure of what it was . . . that he was haunted by something, some memory or experience which he wished to relate.

I did not know how I would approach him again or how I would ever learn his secret, but I need not have worried. A few days later while Sister Lena was resting after lunch, I heard a light tap at the front door. I found Peter Giddings waiting there, dressed in neat western-type clothes and with a straw hat in his hands.

"Missy got time to talk now?" he asked.

"Yes," I said. "Let us walk outside. I think Sister Lena is sleeping."

I closed the screen door quietly.

"Maybe," he said, twisting the hat in his hands, "it rain on us."

I saw that the sun was lost behind the clouds and a gloom hung overhead. "Let's sit in one of the classrooms," I suggested.

I knew that the school term had not yet begun, for I had passed Miss Amanda on the mission compound that morning and she had mentioned the fact that in a few days all the classrooms must be cleaned in preparation for the opening of school.

Now the classrooms stood deserted except for their dusty tables and benches. We went inside the newest mud and cement block one just across the way. Peter sat down on the opposite side of a table from me. Just then the rain began to fall, a few drops at a time as if someone scattered pebbles on the tin roof. I sat quietly, waiting for him to begin.

He folded his hands and stared at me. "Why you come again to our village?"

I had not expected to be questioned but I realized now that he might still be wondering to what extent he could trust me. I glanced down at the table trying to answer honestly. "Because I could not forget this village," I said. "And once you feel close to a place, it somehow becomes part of your concern."

His eyes widened. "You not missionary?" he said, still questioning. "You just interested in our people?"

"Yes," I answered, "that's right."

He smiled and I felt that he believed me. But then he asked, "Why?"

"I don't know exactly," I said, "but it has to do with a memory that has haunted me these many years."

"The memory of your husband?" he asked.

"No," I said. "That memory brought me here before, but once I was here something else happened to me."

His eyes watched unrelentingly.

"It's hard to explain," I said.

He waited.

"When I was here before," I began, "I found a strange identity with the people. They reached out to me and I wanted to understand them. For the first time I felt the real importance of human communication. And as I found that I cared about them, I seemed to sense in them some deep suffering."

"Suffering?" he asked quietly.

"Yes." I paused and as he looked at me I felt that he understood.

He nodded his head and then he seemed to study me, his eyes dark and somber. "What you think is this suffering?"

I shook my head and glanced out toward the jungle beyond. "I am not sure," I said, "but I feel that it has to do with some basic need of the human spirit."

"Yes," he said, his voice very low.

The rain sprinkled a bit harder, yet as if still reluctant to fall.

"Now I have returned," I said, "to try to understand."

He studied his hands. "I know," he said, "that my people suffer in many ways, for we have many needs."

"Yes," I said. "I want to know about the people and their needs. What has changed in the village since I was here before? What has improved, what remains the greatest need?"

He looked at me as if he did not know where to begin.

"Perhaps you will tell me what has happened to you," I suggested.

"Yes." He glanced down. Then as he raised his eyes and spoke he seemed to measure his words. "I'm an evangelist now," he said.

"A worker for the mission?" I asked, surprised.

"Yes, I go out to villages in the bush to take the message of the Bible."

He hesitated and seemed to be waiting for my reaction. I thought of what I had learned of the pagan beliefs of this man and his fear of the evil spirits at the time of the plane accident. I wondered what it meant for a tribal chief, the defender of the ancestral spirits, to be converted to a different religion. Then I remembered what this man had told me about being "put down" by his own tribe.

"Why have you become an evangelist?" I asked.

He frowned. "It all started some time ago, soon after I lost my chiefdom. I begin to listen more to the missionary and I think about what he teach."

He sighed and deep wrinkles appeared across his forehead, yet I felt that he wanted to tell me. "Then one day I got sick," he said, "awful sick and God spoke to me in a dream."

"Did you just feel that He spoke to you," I asked, "or did you see God in this dream?"

"I see Him," he said.

Perhaps Peter saw a flash of doubt in my face because his eyes widened and he insisted. "I see Him all right."

"What did He look like?" I asked gently.

"He was a tall man with a stern face."

"Was He a white man or a black man?"

Peter glanced at me and sighed again. "He was a white man," he said. "And in the dream," he went on, "God spoke straight out to me. He said, 'Peter, you got to give up everything what stands in your way, everything what keeps you from being a good and faithful servant to me.' "

Peter nodded. "That's what He said. And I knew what he meant."

"You knew what it was that He wanted you to give up?"

His shoulders sagged. "I knew all right."

The rain came down hard now. Across the school grounds and along the path everyone had run for cover. We sat boxed in by four sheets of water as the rain splashed from the tin roof in search of the ground. The musty smell of dust and dampness surrounded us. Mr. Giddings went on telling me about his dream.

"God demanded," he said, "that I give up my wives."

"How many wives did you have?"

"Ten."

"And you felt that God asked you to give up *all* your wives?"

"All but one," he said. "My first wife I could keep."

"Is this what the mission teaches?"

"Yes," he said, "and I had been . . . sorta a Christian for some time but I had refused to give up my wives."

Peter clasped and unclasped his hands. "That night in the dream, the Lord, He say to me, 'Peter, you gotta go and preach for me.' I was shocked. I kept raising up in my bed and asking, 'How I gonna do that?' But the Lord, He kept after me, and they tell me later that I was in a heavy sweat and I kept pushing up in my bed crying out, 'How I gonna do that?' 'til finally I fell back into a deep sleep."

The man paused, remembering the experience. "My wives they shake me and roll me about but they can't rouse me at all. They think I'm dead."

"Your illness must have made you fall into a coma," I said.

"I guess so," he said. "Anyway my wives went into the village for my people and when they all come back, I woke up. They cried out in fear and run 'cause they think I already rising from the dead. But I called them back and told them 'bout my dream."

He put his hands to his face a moment and then went on. "My people, they shake their heads and talk, and they go in and out of the hut and whisper and talk some more. Then they say to me, 'You sure you see the white man's God?' And I say, 'Yes, I'm sure.' And they say, 'You must be very sick.' And they put me in a hammock and carry me to the mission dispensary. The nurse, she give me medicine and send me home."

He stretched back and then sank forward on his elbows. "It take me long time to get well," he said, "and all during that time. . . ."

He paused and for a while he seemed completely exhausted by the memory of it all.

"What happened during that time," I prompted, "when you were trying to recover?"

His black eyes opened wide like windows to his mind. "The Lord, He kept after me. He won't let me rest none. He say over and over, 'Peter, you gotta preach for me, but you know what you gotta do before you fit to preach for me.' "

Peter took a deep breath and leaned back a little. "For long time I fight with this dream, but finally I made my decision. I called my first wife to my bedside and told her I would keep her but all the other nine wives gotta go back to their families."

"What about their children?" I asked.

"I let my wives take the youngest ones," he said, "all the ones under school age. But soon as the younguns old enough for school they got to come back to me."

"How many children do you have?" I asked.

"There be seventeen in all," he said, "and eight of them go to the mission school."

"Your first wife has to care for all of those?"

"Yes," he said sadly. "It hard job for her."

The rain had slackened some now and fell like large tears around us.

"What did your wives think of your decision?"

He shook his head. "They didn't like it. They argued. They said it wasn't a fair thing for me to do to them. "

He sighed, his eyes dropping despondently. "When I wouldn't change my mind, they cried. They say even if they with their family they gonna be lonely." He paused as if remembering their words. "They say that being lonely is a deep down hurt."

"I think I understand how they felt," I said.

"Maybe you can," he said, "but not me. In the first part of

my mind I have only what God say to me. So I make all my wives go with me to the missionary. We have white man preacher here at that time and I want to make sure that all my wives hear what I say to him."

A stillness hung in the sullen air and in the heat that rose, perspiration stood out on Peter's face.

"I tell him everything, how God spoke to me and what He say. And while my wives stood quiet behind me I tell him what I was gonna do."

"What did the missionary say?" I asked.

The frown that Peter wore around his dark eyes eased a little. "Oh, he was very happy. He say it was a fine thing I was doing. He tell me he start right away to teach me to be evangelist." Peter shifted position on the hard bench and went on. "My wives, they start to pack their things. They work slow, and they grumble. The ones who had to go long way to their families in another village say they can't walk so far with all their pots and wrappers and things on their heads, and their babies on their backs too. They find excuses not to go one day and then the next, 'cause they say they got no reason to go at all."

The man stared down at the table and ran his thumbnail along a ridge in the wood. "I meant to keep my word to the Lord," he said quietly, "but on the third day I took back my second wife. She my favorite. All night we lay on my mat and cry."

The sun broke through the clouds like a harsh blow administered from above and the sounds of voices as people resumed their outdoor activities seemed to jeer at us. But Peter sat almost lost in thought.

"How could God ask me to give up those I love?" He looked at me, his eyes solemn and sad. "How could He ask me to go back on my duty to care for my wives?"

Peter spoke quietly, his voice unsteady. "How could He ask

me to drive them away when they love me?" He shook his head. "I have tried and tried to understand, but in my heart I cannot."

"What did you do?" I asked, at last.

He sighed with a weariness that seemed to come from the depths of his soul. "I prayed to God and ask He forgive my sins and my questions."

"What happened to your wives?"

"I sent 'em away, and then I began to preach for the Lord." He folded his hands, a haunted look on his face.

"Why did you do it?" I asked.

He bit his lip. "I don't know," he said. "Some folks say I got religion 'cause the tribe put me down as chief."

He put his hand against his head. "But I know I had to do it," he said quietly. "I had to 'cause the missionary say the Lord God He love me and I got to do as He say."

For a long time he sat silent, his head bowed. When finally he glanced up at me and I saw the desperate look on his face, I felt myself trembling and for a moment I could not speak.

I rose and stood at the window opening looking out. In the distance I saw the church. And as I stood there I thought of this man, Peter, and the other converts like him. I thought of Sister Lena and the missionaries she represented. I thought of the complexity of the results of a western religion introduced into a pagan society. I thought of how in the hard life of the jungle a man needs many wives to help him grub a minimum living and rear even a few of his children to adulthood.

I thought too about the power of a dream when one feels driven by a supreme authority. I thought about the tragedy of any and every defeated spirit, and how one must search for individual identity, as well as unity, within the human race.

And as I stared out, in the distance I could see the old cemetery with its weeds that were trying to claim the graves of the missionaries and the natives as one.

Twelve

ON SUNDAY I went to church. Since my arrival I had promised Pastor Bypou on a number of occasions that I would. The night he entertained Sister Lena and me for dinner, one afternoon when he called on me, and several times when I saw him visiting among the dispensary patients he had said, "I hope you will come to church while you are here."

"Yes," I promised, "I will come."

Now it seemed more important than ever to go, not just out of courtesy to Pastor Bypou but because I felt anxious to know if the message of the church reached the people as it had the old chief. In what way had the stern teachings of the ways of the Lord affected the other people? Would many of them come? Would they sing and feel rejoiced, fulfilled, or dejected?

I walked to the church alone. The morning air, clear and warm, stirred the leaves on the trees along the path. The sun shone bright against the damp ground. A few students, having returned to the compound prior to the opening of school, came across the lawns. Men in neat western-style pants and shirts came along the path followed by women in clean wrappers and children wearing whatever little shirts or dresses they owned. Most of the men wore sandals. Some of the women and all of the children were barefoot. I recognized many former dispensary patients and I wondered if they were truly converts or if they came out of loyalty to the mission, perhaps in appreciation for the medical help they had received.

I stood for a moment on the porch of the church and watched the people go in. From the door I saw that the women and the girls sat on the left side of the wide aisle that ran down the center of the stone floor, and that the men and boys sat on the right. I went in and found a seat on one of the wooden benches near the back, beside an old woman who sat alone. The church was crowded, but the Andersons, who came in late, found space to sit together with the men on the right.

Sister Lena, who had explained to me earlier that she felt more tired than usual, did not appear. Anyway she had her Bible and several denominational periodicals that she read whenever she could find time. Perhaps these helped to comfort her and fill her religious needs.

Pastor Bypou, dressed in his white vestry robes, stood at the pulpit now and with a deep voice greeted the people in their native Kpelle language. They seemed to listen carefully.

But as I could not follow what he said, I studied his face while he talked, and wondered just what he, as a native minister, meant to the people. "He's a good man," Sister Lena had told me, "a strong man who does much to guide the people." Yet I felt from some of the other remarks that she made about him that she did not often find inspiration in his sermons.

He had grown up in a mission school, received some extra training as a preacher, and had been given the job at the little village church when the mission decided to begin turning over more of its evangelistic tasks to Africans. His wife, with little formal education, worked hard caring for their children as best she knew how. Several times since the evening when the nurse and I had dined there I had passed her mud hut on the mission compound. I always stopped to greet her where she worked in the side yard, usually pounding cassava to make fufu to add to her family's daily soup. Quiet and unassuming she did all the chores while her husband filled his role as pastor to the people. He counseled the patients confined at the dispensary, rang the church bell early every morning to remind the people to pray, and walked through the village trying to win souls for Christ. He seemed to take his work very seriously and I felt a deep sincerity and dedication in his manner.

I thought of the afternoon a few days before when he stopped by to visit me. We had sat in the living room and exchanged pleasantries as one might do during any pastoral call. Finally I asked him to tell me what it meant to one to change from a pagan religion to Christianity.

"It means a step up higher," he said.

He glanced down as if nervous in his attempt to discuss a sensitive subject. "A pagan man is a religious man," he said, "but he depends on the spirits of his ancestors to help him live a good life for the Great God."

"Does he believe that these spirits can do him both good and harm?" I asked.

He nodded. "His whole life is surrounded by these spirits."

"Then how can a man break away?"

"As soon as a man knows that he can talk directly to the Christian God he ought to be willing to give up belief in the power of family spirits."

"Isn't that difficult for a man to do," I asked, "if he feels his whole life to be influenced by these ancestral spirits?"

"Yes," he said, "sometimes a man might say he's a Christian but still he lives in fear that some of his old spirits might become angry because he cast them out and they might do him harm."

"Then what do you tell the people?"

He crossed his legs and sat up straighter. "I tell them they've got to give up their beliefs of the past and listen to the Lord God."

"Do the people listen to you?"

"They hear me," he said, but there was something uncertain in the way he nodded his head.

However, I remembered having been told by an African that a religious leader usually receives the same respect from the people as their tribal chief receives. Thereafter Pastor Bypou must feel great pride in his position. Perhaps too he could reach the people and give them even more of a sense of hope than was possible for a white outsider to do.

I looked around the church now wondering whether or not he was reaching the people. The women, most of whom had their hair wrapped in colorful kerchiefs, sat with their hands folded, or with babies on their laps. One young mother took out her breast and offered it to her whimpering child. Another woman lifted a fretting toddler to her knee. The larger children needed no care but rather sat quietly on the hard wooden benches which looked darkened with years of use. Some of the men and boys watched the minister but others, as if in deep thought, studied the floor.

A musty odor filled the church. Through the window openings, placed high in the stone wall, I saw clouds gathering. Most of the light in the church seemed to come in from the door, as if forming a path to the pulpit where a dull red altar cloth hung down.

Pastor Bypou read from the Bible now and I listened to the strange tones of his tribal language coming from behind his thick lips. His large eyes stared from the depths of his expressive face. He gestured with his hands, his voice loud and persuasive.

Later the people sang. There was no music from the organ which sat in one corner. The minister had explained to me a few days earlier that the organ, a gift from the airlines to the mission at the time of the plane accident, had been long in disrepair. But the people sang a hymn that had been translated into Kpelle words they could understand. I stood with them while they sang and I felt swept up by their emotion and by what seemed to be a tone of pleading in their voices.

When the minister gave his sermon, first in Kpelle, I stared at him wondering again what he was saying. As his enthusiasm grew, authority seemed to flare from his piercing black eyes and he struck the altar with his hand to give greater emphasis to his message. The people began to shift restlessly in their seats and from time to time they cast furtive glances at the minister.

When he repeated his sermon in English, as required by the mission, I began to understand their apprehension. At first his words seemed to be a rhetorical plea for world peace. "If all the world leaders would stop thinking only of themselves," he said, "they could help us find peace."

He went on, reducing the complexities of the world situation to what sounded like a scrap between selfish boys. "But the tragedy is," he shouted, "that for all their quarreling and talk they don't have the answer. Only the Lord has the answer and who is going to make them listen to the Lord?"

As he warmed to his subject concerning the need for humility and obedience, he spoke more sharply. "We all got to do things in the ways of the Lord," he said.

Then leaning forward he pointed his finger at his audience. "Do you think your way of doing things is better than the Lord's way?"

He shook his head. "You have got to quit thinking you know better than the Lord."

He paused a moment. "If you go to the dispensary but you won't do like Sister Lena tells you, you won't get any medicine."

Gesturing with both hands, he went on. "And if you go to Monrovia and speak out against the government you are going to get put in jail."

He stared out meaningfully and then wiped the perspiration from his forehead. "I tell you," he went on, "God too wants you to humble yourself and obey His laws."

Then he pointed his finger again at the crowd. "Hear me," he shouted. "You are sinners, we are all sinners in the eyes of the Lord."

He pounded the edge of the altar. "God wants to help His believers, but He is going to punish His sinners," he lashed. "Punish. Do you hear? He is going to punish *all* sinners!"

The people sat quietly, but with each loud threat from the minister, a shudder seemed to run through the crowd. With slumped shoulders and troubled faces, they sat as if pressed by the fire of hell from above. And as I watched I thought sadly of all the forces that controlled them.

In the past, tribal law and fear of evil spirits had constrained them, guiding their every movement in life. Also the slaves returning to Africa from America, who settled along the coast, had fought the bush people and brought them under national rule. Then the white missionaries had tried to replace their primitive culture and pagan beliefs with western ideas in the name of Christianity. Nowhere in their history had there been any real emphasis put on an individual's worth as a human being. Always there had been some force telling them what to do or what to think. They had little opportunity to express any self-dignity inherent in their nature.

A cloud blotted out the sun completely now and in the dull light the church seemed suddenly cold. Once again I heard a pleading tone in the voices of the people as they sang the last hymn. And the colorful wrappers that had been gay in the sunlight now looked faded and old. Perhaps on other Sundays the minister spoke of love and hope and the promise of redemption, but today my heart felt heavy too as I watched the people.

They moved somberly as they came out of the church. At the door the Andersons greeted me in their friendly way. "It's good to see you here," said Erwin. Marcia smiled, and without comment about the service they politely shook hands with the minister and then went along the path toward their house.

Miss Amanda approached me. "You see," she said, indicating the crowd, "the people are mostly good folks. They come to church just like Pastor Bypou tells them to do." She spoke quietly and I could not tell from her expression to what extent she approved or disapproved his authority.

Many of the people spoke to me and I found myself wishing I knew their thoughts. Did they come to church only because of the request of the minister, or were they seeking some inspiration, or trying to gain new courage to see them through that week? Could such a sermon give them confidence or hope?

Pastor Bypou stood in front and greeted the people in Kpelle as they came out. He shook hands in the tribal manner by clicking middle fingers with them. From his frown I felt that he scolded one old woman who had not bothered to cover her flat dangling breasts. And to several others he seemed to give a firm warning of some kind.

I thought of how he had demanded their obedience to God, their loyalty to the church. I could see why those who had been helped medically might feel a special duty to accept the beliefs of the mission. I thought of how the minister had warned the people about obedience to the government in order that they might stay out of jail, and how he had admonished them to listen to Sister Lena so that they might not be denied any medical assistance they needed.

I watched the people as they dispersed and went off down the path. They seemed belittled by authority and stunned by the anguish of Christian guilt. I stood there looking after them, thinking of the power of religion in all human lives, a power fostered by the need of everyone to believe in something greater than himself. Yet I wondered if one could truly find a deep spiritual peace without first finding inside himself his own human resources with which to build. And what motivates one to look within himself and search for such resources?

After Pastor Bypou shook my hand and finally turned away from his last parishioner, I noticed how troubled he looked and I wondered whether he felt that the church was doing enough to help the people.

Must they be commanded, or was there another way?

Thirteen

"THE PEOPLE amaze me," I said to Sister Lena, when I came in from a walk early one afternoon.

"How do you mean?" she asked.

"Even though they are poor they always have something to give." I showed her the cassava roots a man gave me when I met him on the path, the yams an old woman pressed into my hands as I passed her hut, and the strange little raffia slingshot with a tiny woven basket for stones a girl had made for my son.

Gami stood at the kitchen door. "While you out," she said to me, "Duana come and bring whole stalk of bananas."

"A whole stalkful!" I exclaimed.

"Yes, ma'am," she said, and she brought them in for me to see.

"They are beautiful," I said, "but I don't understand."

Gami smiled. "He say it terrible thing you want bananas and you not find in our village."

Sister Lena sniffed. "I don't know about those Moslems," she said. "They are traders. He might want something big in return." She rose then and started back to the dispensary.

Gami frowned and shrugged her shoulders, but when the nurse was gone she turned to me.

"Duana say, would you like to come to Moslem service in the village?"

"Today?"

"Yes, ma'am."

"What time?"

"He say, one o'clock."

I looked at my watch. "It's almost two o'clock now."

"Yes, ma'am," she said. "I not know where to find you sooner."

"I'll hurry," I said, and I rushed into the village.

I assumed that there must be a small mosque that I had not noticed before. I walked all around, through areas off the main path to the other side of the village, but I did not see anything that looked like a mosque. Finally I found a child who spoke English, and I asked her to direct me. I followed her around mud huts built close together. There were no streets and the grounds kept cleared of grass were muddy and dotted with rain puddles.

The hut where the Moslem service was in progress looked like all the others. It was mud, round, and had a thatched roof. Beside the doorway many pairs of shoes and sandals waited. I stood there wondering if I should go in. Through the open door I saw the people in their long robes kneeling on straw mats. They touched the beads dangling from their necks as they prayed.

I hesitated at the door, reluctant to go in and disturb them, feeling that I should not. Suddenly the service was over and the congregation poured out. Many had no shoes waiting at the door. The women, as colorful as wild flowers in their tobs, smiled at me and moved to one side.

Duana, dressed in his royal blue robe, came over, bowed to

me, and introduced his wives and children. I offered to take a picture of them together. Duana was delighted. But as we talked one of his wives slipped away.

We found her hiding shyly behind a hut. Duana spoke to her in Arabic and then in Kpelle. "She don't want to be in picture," he said.

"Why not?" I asked.

He frowned and pointed at the camera.

"Is she afraid?"

He nodded.

"But she need not be afraid," I protested. "My camera can't hurt her." I turned to her to explain.

She scowled at me.

"No," said Duana, "she not understand you."

Then he spoke to her again in Arabic, but she kept shaking her head.

"She is afraid evil spirits live in your black box," he said to me.

"I don't wish to frighten her," I said.

He threw up his arms. "I have told her many times that is not the kind of thing we need to be afraid of."

The other wife and all six of the children waited with us in the sun. Beads of perspiration showed on all their faces. But the young wife stood firm, her hands on her hips.

"Perhaps we shouldn't upset her," I said to Duana. "Shall we take the picture without her?"

"Oh, no," he said. "She my favorite wife. I want her in it."

Still frowning, he took her aside and talked and scolded and talked some more. Finally he went inside his house and came out with a beautiful white and gold tob draped over his arm.

He was grinning. "She say she'll be in picture if I let her wear new dress."

The young wife took her time getting ready while we all

waited in the hot sun. In a most complicated fashion she wound the lovely fabric around and around her slim body over the old tob she wore, all the time holding her head proudly. But when she finally stood beside her husband, his other wife, and all his children, she would not smile. Apparently that was not part of the bargain and she had found her own way of demanding what she considered to be her rights.

When I had finished taking the picture and started to go, Duana stopped me. "Wait," he said. "I have something for your son." He went into his house.

"But Duana," I called after him, "you have been very generous . . . the meat, the bananas . . . you really shouldn't give me anything more."

I thought of what Sister Lena said about the Moslems being traders and I wondered if this time he would ask a big price.

He came out with his hands cupped together. I could not tell what he held at first, but when he opened his hands a little I saw a tiny animal.

"I hear that American children have 'most everything," he said apologetically, "but maybe your son not have a baby porcupine."

The tiny creature hovered in his hand, frightened but not trying to get away. It looked fragile, new, and pink, but the little quills that covered its body stood out like sharp needles.

"My son doesn't have everything," I said. "And I know he would love such a pet."

Then as gently as I could I tried to explain about my long voyage home, about customs regulations and the difficulty of taking an animal into my country. I could not be sure that he understood. He nodded but he looked disappointed.

"Before you leave our village," he said, "I'll bring something for your son."

A few days later he came to see me. He stepped onto the

porch with a twinkle in his eyes, as if he had some important news to share. When he was settled in a chair he smiled. "I want you to know," he began, "that I think about what you say many days ago when you first come."

I looked at him, wondering to what he referred.

Just then Sister Lena came out on the porch. "Duana," she asked in a crisp voice, "how much do you want for those bananas you left here the other day?"

He frowned and shook his head. "I not want pay," he said. "I brought to Missy."

"That's nice," she said wryly. "You always charge a lot for the things you bring to me."

Duana did not answer her, so that after standing there a moment longer she turned and went back inside.

The Moslem leaned back in his chair then and folded his arms glumly.

"Please," I said, hoping to respark his enthusiasm, "tell me your news."

He sighed. "It 'bout my boy," he said.

Then a glimmer of light showed in his eyes. "I been to see the head man at the mission school and I ask him to take my son this year."

"That's wonderful," I said. "What about your daughter?"

He shook his head. "She needed at home."

"But Duana," I cried, "don't you want education for your daughter as well?"

"I guess she don't need it much."

I thought for a moment about how I might convince him. "When your boy grows up," I said, "don't you suppose he will want to marry an educated girl who will know better how to help him?"

He nodded. "I guess so."

"Well," I said, "so will all the other boys who are going to the mission school."

He studied me solemnly. "I see what you mean," he said. Then he laughed. "Next year I send my girl to school." He leaned back and clasped his hands together. "You think education is good for everybody?"

"Yes."

"Why?"

I sat forward wondering how to explain. "When we learn to read," I said, "we can find many ways to help ourselves."

He nodded and then, as if still trying to convince himself, he said, "The mission helps my people here with medicine, I guess it all right to send my son to mission school."

I watched his dark brow wrinkle. "Too bad we Moslems not have a mission school."

"But surely," I said, "learning to read and write is the important thing."

He remained silent for a few moments. "Yes," he said, "but I think many times about religion."

He folded his arms. "Here in this village we got people who still worship ancestor spirits. We got people who believe like the missionaries say, and we got small group of Moslems. I look around and I see all the people much the same. They live the same. They suffer the same."

He shook his head. "I think about it many times. I wonder why one man believe one way and another man believe another way. I see the pagan man live in fear of losing favor of the spirits that live between him and the Great God. Yet he believe in his fetish priest and know he can trust him to do exactly as he teach. I see man turned Christian and put aside ancestor spirits and learn to pray directly to the Great God like the preacher say. But some times he find that Christian leaders not do like they teach. Then the man worry and fear that maybe all what the Christian leaders say not true and maybe he need help of old spirits after all."

He paused. "Then the Christians talk about the Holy Spirit

and say this the link between God and man. They say this Holy Spirit lead man along a right path to God and that it don't make hard time for him like the ancestor spirits might do. But then the Christian leaders talk a lot about the need to fear God, and how He gonna punish sinners."

He rubbed his head. "It mix me up. One day He a God what love you and next day you got to fear Him."

Laughing he clapped his hands together. "Many people not understand. I say it simpler to be Moslem. Mohammed passed down laws for all people to follow, laws direct from God."

As he talked Duana folded and unfolded his cornshuck hat that he held on his lap.

"Still, like I say, I wonder many times about religion," he went on quietly. "I see every man have some good days and many hard times. I see how men laugh and cry and then someday . . . everybody got to die."

He sat silent for a moment as if lost in thought. Then he glanced up at me. "Now I ask you." He leaned forward and gestured with his hands. "I ask you, which the big man, Jesus or Mohammed?"

I pondered his question. "Both men were outstanding leaders," I said. "Each brought important messages to the world."

"I know," he said. "But which one the big man?"

"The answer depends," I said, "on whether one is a Christian or a Moslem."

"You know I a Moslem," he said, "but I want to know for sure."

I hesitated as I watched his disturbed face, his sad eyes. "What in life do we ever know for sure?" I asked.

He shook his head. "I don't know." Then glancing down for a moment he became silent.

"When you were here before," he said slowly, as if reminiscing, "I remember I had just set out some rubber saplings. I thought for sure by the time they big enough to tap, the road into Sanoyea would be finished so I could get my latex to market." He nodded. "I thought, *for sure.*"

He sighed and sank down in his chair. "The road still not finished."

I thought of the government official who was a guest at the home of Pastor Bypou the night I had dined there. He too had spoken of the need to get the road finished.

"How do you manage?" I asked Duana.

"I got many barrels of latex stacked in back of my house," he said. "I hope in dry season I find way to get them out."

He leaned forward on the arm of his chair. "You right," he said. "No matter how much we think things gonna work out, or how much we willing to believe, we can't know *for sure.*"

He sounded despondent, almost without hope. "But seems like there ought to be something . . . something everybody can believe in."

Hesitating, he gestured with his hands. "Maybe a spirit, or a feeling, some truth, something that could bring all people together to love, to really care about each other."

Then sighing deeply he dropped his hands. "But where we gonna look to find such a thing?"

Seeing his long face I felt overwhelmed with his sadness, the sadness of the people.

"Can you believe," I asked, trying desperately to think of what I ought to say, what I really wanted to say, "that even though we don't know all the answers in life, that perhaps there is some reason to have faith, maybe first in ourselves and then in our fellow men?"

He studied me, his eyes narrowed. "Do you really believe in love and friendship," he asked, "in freedom and justice?"

I nodded. "I'd like to."

"You think every man is meant to find some happiness?"

I felt the stillness around us, the quiet of the afternoon. Perhaps I waited too long to answer him, but finally I said, "Yes, Duana, I believe that everyone must have hope for a happier tomorrow. Otherwise the distress and injustices of every day would become intolerable."

He sighed and clasped his hands together. "Yes," he said, "but some time I wonder where to find the courage needed to live each day."

"It is not easy," I agreed.

He remained silent a long time as if suffering uncertainty. "No man knows for sure that he can," he said. Then he added, "But I think each man just *got* to find that courage inside hisself."

Nodding his head decisively he rose. "I sorry I stay too long," he said. "But I think we find great good in our talk."

From his pocket he took out an envelope. "The reason I stop by," he said, "was to ask you please tell your son howdy plenty and give him this."

With a smile then he went out and down the path.

When I entered the living room Sister Lena looked up from her desk. "Well, what did Duana really want?" she asked.

As I stood there I wondered. "I don't know, for sure," I said. But suddenly I felt as if he had opened a new door in my search for a better understanding of the people. And later when I read his letter to my son I found in it his only request.

> Dear Frank,
>
> I a poor man and I got nothing right to give you. But I think of something I can do. Many times as years go by I will stand at your father's grave and pray for you.

I hope some day you will come. Many things not yet right in our village. Maybe you have wisdom to help make right. So in time that pass before we meet you, will you pray for us?

Your friend,
Duana

Fourteen

AT BREAKFAST one morning I told Sister Lena about a woman's organization to whom I had spoken after my last visit in Sanoyea and how, when they learned of my plan to return to Liberia, they had given me $100 "to help someone in the village."

"I can see many needs," I said, "but I wonder if you have a suggestion?"

The nurse thought for a moment while she finished drinking her coffee. "Yes," she said, "there is a special person you could help."

"Who?" I asked.

"Do you remember Alice," she asked, "the woman who prepares the formula for the orphan babies?"

"Yes," I answered, thinking of the attractive, sturdy woman whom I often saw when she came to fill the bottles.

"Alice has a daughter I think you should meet," said the nurse, as she rose from the table. "Come."

We went out and down the path to the far side of the village. There we stopped in front of a neat square hut where Sister Lena knocked at the door. A girl who stood on her knees answered. In the instant that I saw her well-developed body I felt the shock of having to look down at her. Yet almost immediately my eyes were drawn to her face, for it was a pretty face, oval and smooth as a plum.

"My name Comfort," she said shyly. "You like to come in?" She opened the door wider.

Sister Lena and I stepped inside. As the girl moved back on her knees to let us enter she grasped a nearby chair and pulled herself up. She motioned for us to sit in the two better chairs across from her.

When she was settled, her smile turned on slowly. Her lips parted showing her even white teeth which contrasted beautifully with her brown skin. Then as the glow spread across her face it seemed almost to reach out like the touch of a friendly hand. But it was her big black eyes that dominated her face, and even as she smiled they held that same deep somber look that I saw wherever I went.

When the nurse introduced me the girl nodded. "Yes," she said, "I see you that first day you come to our village."

Her legs, withered below the knees and dusty from crawling, dangled down, but her deformed feet did not quite touch the floor.

"I at the door," she said, "when all the people and the hammock pass by."

She clasped her hands together and studied me. "When you wave from the hammock," she said with a shy smile, "I think you waving to me." She ducked her head but when she glanced up I saw the question still on her face.

"The people were very kind," I said. I could not tell her that I had not seen her from the swinging net. Nor had I known before now that a crippled child lived in the village.

"Comfort," the nurse said to the girl now, "how old are you?"

The girl blinked her big eyes. "My Mama say it been fourteen rain times since I born."

"How long have you been crippled?" the nurse went on.

Comfort glanced down at the clay floor. The smile flickered from her face. "Since I baby," she said. "Mama say I have strange sickness and my legs not grow right."

As we talked with the crippled girl, her mother Alice, an old grandmother, and four smaller children crowded in from the back of the house to greet us.

Alice smiled. "Thank you for coming to our home," she said. The old woman bobbed her head at us and then went to sit on a stool in one corner. The children sat around on the dirt floor.

"I understand that Comfort went to school last year," said Sister Lena.

Alice nodded.

I looked at the girl, wondering how she had managed.

"Yes," Comfort answered, her smile creeping back to light her face. "When government open little school in hut nearby, I crawl there every day."

"You crawled there?" I asked.

"Yes," she said simply.

Alice spoke up. "I wanted her to go to mission school, but she too heavy for me to tote on my back, and it too far for her to crawl."

The girl cast her eyes down but some pride showed on her face as she said, "I learning to read now."

"Yes," said Alice, smiling, "you learning just fine."

"Do you have a book?" I asked.

"She have one book," said Alice. "She read to the little ones."

I looked again at the girl's face. "Would you like to read for me?" I asked.

Comfort glanced at me and then dropped her eyes. Finally she nodded. "I like."

Then she slipped down out of her chair and with her body erect she crawled across the floor on her knees. The hut was divided into four rooms and Comfort scurried into the back room. "I get my book," she said.

"Can't someone get it for you?" I asked, looking around at the other children all of whom sat idly.

"Oh, no," said Comfort. "I keep it in my box." It was clear that she did not allow the smaller children to plunder among her few possessions.

No one rose to help her. Alice smiled as if pleased that her daughter could do some things for herself. The old grandmother, who watched from her stool in the corner, did not speak and I felt that she did not understand the conversation.

The chairs and the stool were the only furniture in the room. Curtains of red printed fabric hung over the doorways that led into two smaller rooms at either side. We sat in a center room at the front of the house.

Comfort opened a wooden door and crawled into a large room across the back. Through the doorway I saw her pull a small cardboard box from under a cot and search inside. After taking out a book she hurried back. Pushing her chair nearer to me, she put the book on my lap in order to have both her hands free to pull herself up.

When she had swung around in her chair she reached out for the book, which I noticed was a second grade reader.

"My teacher let me borrow book for summer vacation," she said. "I read most of it already."

She turned to a page near the back to show me how far she had gone. Beginning there with the next story, she read about a boy and a girl and a game they played with a ball. Nursing each word she glanced at me out of the corner of her eye as if to make sure I was attentive. As the story progressed, telling of the running activities of the children, she glanced down at her withered legs and her enthusiasm for reading seemed to wane. When she finished the page she sighed and closed the book.

"You are learning very well," I said, amazed at how well she read after only one year of training.

At first she did not seem to hear me, then slowly her thoughts moved from the facts of the story to accept my compliment. "Thank you," she said quietly.

Her mother smiled at her, and then said to the nurse, "The new government school not so good as the mission school. It just a little hut with a few tables and benches. The teacher not show up every day. I don't know how good a teacher he is. I know he lose all the papers 'bout what Comfort do, but he say she can study this year as second grade student." Alice turned to her daughter. "School starts again next week."

Comfort nodded, but no enthusiasm showed on her face.

"Will you be glad to go back to school?" asked Sister Lena.

"Yes," she said, without expression.

"It hard for her," said her mother. "Some time she come home with bleeding knees or a thorn in her leg."

As her mother spoke, Comfort stared at the dirt floor and pulled at her dress, trying to cover her scarred knees.

The nurse studied the girl. "When was the last time you went to church?" she asked.

Comfort shook her head.

"She don't remember the church," her mother answered. "She not see the church long time now, not since she grow too heavy for me to tote on my back."

"I wish much to go to church," said Comfort, glancing at the nurse. "I hear tell that Pastor Bypou have many things to tell the people and he say everybody ought to go."

"Yes," said the nurse, "that's right."

We talked for a while longer and by the time we rose to go the girl's smile had found its way back to her face. She shook my hand. "You come to see me again?" she asked.

"Yes," I promised, "I'll do that."

As we walked back through the village Sister Lena sighed. "There are many needs," she said, "but I thought you might like Comfort and want to spend that money to help her in some way."

"Yes," I said, "she is a lovely girl, and life has certainly been cruel to her."

The nurse nodded. "I guess she gets enough to eat," she said, "but I'm sure there are many other things she needs, like clothes, books, maybe a blanket for her cot."

"Yes," I said. But as we walked along I thought of how much she needed a renewed spirit, a chance to do something without feeling embarrassed or disgraced as she obviously felt in her attempt to go to school.

Later as Sister Lena and I sat on the porch of her house in the heat of the afternoon, I kept thinking about Comfort. The nurse put her head back and seemed to doze. I stared out beyond the screen. In the quiet no one moved along the path. What could be done for Comfort to renew her spirit, I wondered?

Suddenly I heard a sound coming along the path, and looking out I saw a small boy running by with a stick in his hand. He was rolling an old rusty wheel.

An idea flashed into my mind. "A wheel chair," I said aloud. "Of course that's the answer."

The nurse stirred. "What's that?" she asked, "Did you say something?"

"Yes," I said, my excitement mounting. "A wheel chair for Comfort would not cost more than about $100 and if she had one she could roll to school."

"Roll to school?" The nurse blinked and sat up.

"Yes," I said. "Perhaps she could roll all the way to the mission school."

Sister Lena, fully awake now, pushed a strand of hair from her face. "That would be good," she said.

Then she frowned. "I don't know though," she went on. "She might not be able to roll herself such a long distance. You know how rough the path is, and it's full of ruts."

"That's true," I said. "But perhaps Alice would be able to push her."

"Maybe." Sister Lena nodded her head.

She leaned back and then added, "If she could get to school, she could also get to church."

"Perhaps that would mean a great deal to her," I said.

"I'm sure it would," said the nurse.

A faint breeze stirred, and a bird in a bush just beyond the screen began to sing.

"As soon as I return home," I said, "I'll send a wheel chair."

"That will be fine," said the nurse.

She settled back in her chair and closed her eyes again. I began to think of home and where I might buy a wheel chair.

"How long does it take such things to come here by boat?" I asked.

"About two or three months," she said languidly.

"That's a long time," I said. "I wish Comfort could have it when school opens next week."

Sister Lena opened her eyes and leaning toward me she put out her hand. "That reminds me," she said. "There's a wheel chair here."

"Where?"

"It arrived here not long ago," she said vaguely. "I haven't had time to uncrate it yet."

"That's wonderful," I said. "Couldn't we give that one to Comfort?"

The nurse shook her head.

"Why not?" I asked.

She seemed to think it over. "I don't know," she said. "It was sent here to me."

"To you?" I asked, wondering why she needed a wheel chair.

"Yes," she said. "For use in the dispensary."

"Oh," I said, "you ordered it?"

"No," she said, folding her hands in her lap, "some church women in Pennsylvania wrote and asked me what I needed for the new dispensary. I thought a wheel chair would be useful whenever we have to move a very sick patient."

I felt discouraged. "I suppose you have waited a long time for it to arrive."

"Yes," she said, "a long time."

She leaned back. "In fact there has never been a wheel chair here before."

I sat forward on the edge of my chair. "Perhaps. . . ." I hesitated. "I wonder if you would mind waiting a few more months until my replacement arrived from the States?"

Sister Lena sat silent for a moment thinking about my request.

"It would be nice," I said, "if Comfort could begin this school year with a better chance."

"Yes," said the nurse, "and perhaps she could go to church."

She rose. "I'll find Steven," she said, "and ask him to uncrate the chair."

"That's wonderful," I said, and I followed her outside.

"You do promise to send a replacement as soon as you get home?"

"I promise."

"All right then." She nodded. "Why don't you go and tell Comfort."

"Yes," I said, "I'd like to do that."

I started down the path.

She called after me. "I'll send Steven along with the chair as soon as we have it put together."

I rushed through the village. The sun, though no longer overhead, was still high above the horizon. Deep shadows of the huts lay across the path, shading the children who played here and there.

When I arrived at her house I found the crippled girl alone, holding a doll in her arms. She greeted me with a look of surprise.

"You didn't expect to see me again so soon, did you?"

She shook her head. "Please come in." She flung open the door.

"I glad you come back," she said, pulling herself up in a chair beside the one I took.

"I have something to tell you," I began.

"Please," she interrupted, holding out her doll to me. "When you leave I think I want you to see my baby, but I can't run after you."

As she put the doll on my lap her face beamed with an expression of triumph, as if I had returned in answer to her prayer.

I took up the doll and held it in my hands. I noticed that it was not like the local dolls that most of the children had. They were made of thick brown reed with eyes, nose, and mouth carved out with a knife, and with black hair from an animal of some kind attached to one end to represent the head. But the doll that Comfort owned was a western doll with fair skin, blue eyes, and light brown hair. It wore a neat print dress and tiny shoes and socks.

"Where did you get such a lovely doll?" I asked.

"A mission lady gave to me," she said quietly.

"It's a nice toy," I said, glancing at the strange possessive expression on the face of the girl. And I wondered why, at her age, she showed such an interest in a doll.

She blinked her big serious eyes. "This my baby," she said, watching me as if asking that I understand how a crippled girl could not look forward to a future with a home and a baby of her own.

Carefully she took the doll from me and nestled it in her arms. As she looked at it and rocked it back and forth she seemed to drift beyond the world of realism to some private world of make-believe. She spoke to it using Kpelle words, and for a moment she seemed to forget that I sat beside her.

As I watched her, I felt a growing concern. It did not seem right that she found it necessary to seek escape deep in a dream. More than ever I wanted to give her new hope.

"Comfort," I said, touching her arm, "I have something to tell you."

Almost reluctantly she turned to me then and listened as I told her about the wheel chair. She stared at me, trying to comprehend.

"I never have my own chair," she said.

"But this will be your very own," I assured her. "And you'll be able to roll to school every day."

"Roll to school?" She smiled.

"Yes," I said, "and perhaps with your mother's help you will be able to roll all the way to the mission school."

"Oh," she clasped her hands with glee, "I'll be able to go anywhere, even to church?"

"I hope so," I said. "If the path isn't too rough."

When I heard the sound of wheels crunching over the ground outside, I rose. "Come," I said. "That must be Steven bringing the wheel chair now."

On her knees Comfort followed me to the door. Clutching the frame, she leaned out to look down the path.

Alice, the grandmother, and the four children came from in back of the hut. I stepped outside and told them about the wheel chair. We all stood there watching Steven come along. The aluminum frame of the wheel chair glistened in the sun. The deep green canvas seat was the color of the jungle that towered just beyond the village. People stopped their work to look, and many followed after Steven, nodding and whispering to each other.

Comfort came out of the house and crawled forward to join the people who arrived with Steven on the wide path in front of where we stood.

I showed her how to lock the wheels, and she struggled up and settled herself in the chair. At first she had difficulty controlling the movement of the wheels.

"Her right hand not so good," said Alice, standing beside me.

I noticed, for the first time, that the girl's right shoulder was higher than her left and that her arm was slightly twisted. "Perhaps with practice she will be able to do better," I said.

"Oh yes," said Alice, "I hope so." But I saw a worried look on her face.

As I watched, it became obvious to me that Comfort could not maintain equal control with her right hand, and the chair kept curving toward the right.

"Sister Lena and I had hoped she might be able to go to the mission school," I said. "But I'm afraid you'll have to help her."

Then she shook her head. "I will try," she said, "but it will be a hard way." She pointed down the path. "I'm afraid it will be too hard. During rain time the path is all ruts and mud puddles."

I looked down the path and had to agree that she was right.

"But at least I can widen the path to the government school," she said cheerfully. "I'm sure I can roll her there."

The girl rolled the chair first one way and then another. When she saw how many ways it would turn she threw back her head and laughed.

More people crowded around to see what the excitement was all about, and they stayed on to cheer. The old grandmother grinned a toothless grin and shook her head in amazement. The four children followed after their big sister and clapped their hands.

Alice smiled now, showing her delight in the happiness on the face of her daughter, for in that moment much of the indignity that she had suffered as a cripple seemed to vanish.

"Comfort, my Comfort," said Alice, clasping her hands together.

I stood beside Alice. "How did you happen to name her Comfort?" I asked.

For a few moments she did not answer but kept staring at her daughter, who rolled and whirled the chair. Finally she seemed willing to turn her thoughts to things of the past, and in a soft voice she spoke of them to me.

"When I first married," she said, "my life full of hard times. I have sickness and my husband lose his rice crop. I turn to prayer, and I pray for a baby to bring me comfort. I think if I have soft little one to hold to my heart, a new joy will start there like a fire to burn out old suffering."

A faint smile formed on her lips, but her eyes continued to follow the girl as she wheeled the chair back and forth through the crowd.

"When my baby come," she went on, "I name her Comfort. It seemed like a good name to me." She paused. "Then when she still very small a strange sickness strike her and all the strength go out her legs and they don't grow much anymore. Then I realize she the one what need comfort and I glad again that I give her that name."

Alice sighed and remained silent for a few moments. "She pitiful to see, crawling and crawling and never no chance to walk. But her body grow heavier and I can't tote her no more. And when I work, I got to leave her home by herself, and she can't play with the other children 'cause they run out and leave her behind."

A new murmur of encouragement for the girl ran through the crowd, but Alice did not seem to notice, and caught up in her thoughts she went on with her story. "I think she got good mind but I don't find no way for her to learn 'till government school start up last year. I want her to go, but I 'fraid for her too."

She paused and shook her head. "Comfort want to go awful bad. She say she gonna crawl to school, nobody gonna stop her. She say she got to do something special herself. I tell her maybe the children might laugh at her not knowing anything from book, and her already so grown her dress getting tight at her breasts."

The people clapped their hands now and called out cheers to Comfort as she made a successful turn.

Alice went on talking. "Comfort say it won't matter if the students laugh at her. Children been laughing at her all her days. She kept after me 'till I cut the little path for her. Then every morning she hold up her dress so not to dirty it and she go right along on her knees."

She sighed. "Many days she come home with bleeding knee or thorn in her leg. And her legs, she drag them so much in the clay, they won't hardly wash clean any more. Comfort, she worry 'cause she say her knees and legs turning grey, and it don't seem right that if she can't be whole and strong like other folks that she also can't be all black like the rest of us."

A small boy in the crowd cried out, "Ho, ho, look at Comfort go!"

As she talked, Alice stared out beyond the crowd, as if in a trance. "Some time I don't know how she keep going."

Because of the cheering voices around us I had to lean closer to hear her next words. "Then one day," she said, "a mission lady gave her a doll and she turned more and more to that. She talk to it and call it her baby. And it seem like the only thing in her life she got left." She stood silent for a while. "I tell her she got to keep crawling to school, but every time she come home with bleeding knees I think hope done left her for good. Some time she just sit and stare out the door, not looking at anything, just sitting and holding that doll."

Alice shook her head sadly and glanced at me. "Did you ever notice," she asked, "that a sadness what comes from a broken down spirit sits heavier than a sadness what comes from any other kind of pain?"

"Yes," I said, and for a moment longer her steady gaze held me a captive of her wisdom.

Then she smiled, a gentle smile moving out slowly from her lips across her face. "But look at her now," she said, and we both turned our attention to Comfort, who had stopped in the midst of the crowd, her face aglow.

A little girl tugged at her arm. "Now give me a turn," she begged.

With a calm dignity, as if from some deep inherent confidence, Comfort shook her head. "No," she said, "it's not a toy." And the smile that spread across her face was a delight to see.

I felt Comfort's new joy and I wished that the women whose money had made the wheel chair possible were there to share the feeling with me, to see how a simple gift, something that could help this child to help herself, had renewed her broken spirit.

Fifteen

A FEW DAYS had passed since Comfort received the wheel chair. Whenever the sun was out she practiced steering it on any hard surface of the path that she could find in front of her house. The news of the "new thing" traveled fast, and many people came to watch her.

Then one morning David, the tall laundry boy who worked for Sister Lena, came to the nurse. "Mama," he said, in a childlike manner hardly in keeping with his size, "you give me bicycle?"

"What do you mean?" the nurse asked. "I don't have any bicycle."

David, wiry and thin, stood before her, his sleeveless blue denim shirt hanging to his bare knees. "I like bicycle," he said, his frown making fine wrinkles across his forehead.

Sister Lena shrugged in dismay. "You know I don't have any bicycle," she said. "And even if I did I would not give it away."

David waited, his muscular arms hanging loosely, covering for the moment his ribs, which usually showed through the slits in the sides of his shirt.

"Now listen, David," the nurse said, studying his face. "If you want a bicycle I could keep part of your salary every month until we had saved enough to buy one. Perhaps I could help you find extra work so that you could earn more."

The tall boy looked at her with big solemn eyes but said nothing.

"A bicycle is very expensive," the nurse went on. "It will take you a long time to save enough."

David shifted his weight from one foot to the other. "I work for you now," he said, "long time."

"Yes, I know," said the nurse. "But I pay you what I can, and I cannot afford to give you expensive gifts."

Shyly, David glanced down. "Comfort never work for you," he said, "and you gave her rolling thing."

The nurse nodded. "Oh, now I see," she said, smiling. "The wheel chair gave you ideas."

"Yes, Mama."

Sister Lena shook her head. "You see what these people are like?" she said to me.

Then turning to David, she tried to explain about the gift of the wheel chair to Comfort—where it had come from and why. "Surely, David, you can see the difference," she said. "You are strong and able to work, but God has afflicted Comfort and she needs the wheel chair to get to school and to church."

David blinked his eyes as he listened, and when he was dismissed he said, "Yes, Mama," and turned away obediently.

The nurse looked distressed. "Some of the people are like children," she said. "They think that all they have to do is ask and things will be given to them."

"Why have they come to think that way?" I asked.

She sat down and sighed. "There are probably several reasons," she said. "But I know some of our missionaries have spoiled them."

"How do you mean?"

"Well," she said, "I know of a nurse who made a point of spoiling the children because she wanted them to love her like a mother."

When Sister Lena mentioned her name I remembered having heard of her on my previous visit, although she had been away on furlough at that time.

"What sort of things did she do?" I asked now.

"All kinds of incredible things," she exclaimed. "Once when a child played hooky from school she gave him candy and hid him under her bed when the teacher came looking for him."

"Surely she couldn't think that was a good attitude to have toward the people," I exclaimed.

"I guess she did," said the nurse. "She kept letting them impose on her, giving them extras all the time. She seemed to love doing it, even though it meant that she used far more than her fair share of the mission budget."

"Why did the mission allow her to do that?"

"I don't know," she said. "Apparently they felt that because she was so well loved she must be doing a good job."

Sister Lena frowned. "Now she has retired and I'm here," she said, "not only with the extra work of the new dispensary, but also with the task of making the people understand that I believe that old way was wrong."

Suddenly I realized better than I had before the plight that Sister Lena faced. Ever since she had been in the mission field she had been confronted with an unfortunate situation that had been building up for years. A kindly motherly nurse had given most of her life to the people of Sanoyea, but in so doing she had coaxed them to lean on her.

"Do you think she was more loving than selfish?" Sister Lena asked me.

"I don't know," I said. But as I thought about it I could see what Sister Lena must mean, that people who coax others to lean on them are perhaps more selfish than altruistic. Can anyone trained to lean on another ever learn to stand on his own?

"It's not easy to make these people see how and why they should be more disciplined," she said, her usual show of firmness evident in her jaw. "How can I make them understand why they should pay something for the medical help I give them? How can I persuade them that any task they undertake should be done well?" She shook her head despondently.

Certainly no one would envy Sister Lena her position. For these years of confronting the petty day to day problems of the people, many of whom expected something for nothing, would be enough to wear down the patience of anyone. I knew she meant well in trying to right the situation.

"Do the Andersons agree with you?" I asked. "Do they try to show the people how to be more responsible?"

"Yes," she said, "I think they want to help the people."

I waited, hoping she would tell me what she felt the young couple were contributing to the advancement of the villagers, but she did not continue.

"Since Marcia is a nurse," I said, "couldn't she be helpful to you in the dispensary?"

"She helps sometimes," said the nurse, "whenever I need her." She folded her arms, and on her face I saw her usual look of self-reliance. I knew it was the look to which the Andersons had become accustomed and that it reflected the attitude of the nurse with which they were trying to cope.

But even as I thought of the long hours of work Sister Lena accomplished every day, of her endless devotion to her task, I could not forget that almost every time I went into the dispensary I heard her scolding some young mother in a way that robbed the woman of her dignity. And I remembered that eventually the mother would turn away, just as David had done, a disconsolate look on her face.

I went out to find David. Perhaps I could learn something more from him.

In the back yard I found him leaning over a long stick of wood, hacking away at it with a large jungle knife.

"Hello," I said, standing beyond the range of the flying chips.

David glanced up and nodded to me, and then bracing the piece of wood with his bare foot he went on chopping.

Smoke rose from around a big black pot which was filled with water. But the fire seemed slow to blaze.

Trying to find a way to begin a conversation I asked David, "What's wrong with the fire? Is that spot too damp from the heavy rains?"

"No," he said. "I cover spot with pieces of tin when it not fire time."

I saw the sheets of tin leaning against the laundry shelter that stood to one side. A mud structure with a tin roof, the shelter was open on all sides to let in air and light. An iron and a tin tub stood on a makeshift table, and numerous lines strung above the table held the clothes still not dry since the last rain.

David picked up the pieces of wood he had cut and began to push them under the pot. "The wood, it new from the bush. It smoke much."

The smoke that billowed up blended with the deep blue of David's long denim shirt, which hung almost to his knees. It was the only garment I ever saw him wear, with the occasional addition of a pair of faded yellow underpants that showed several inches below the edge of his shirt. His shirt always hung loosely from his body, covering as well as it could his thinness.

I stepped closer and tried to talk to him again. "How do you like working here on the mission compound?"

He nodded.

"Did you go to the mission school?" I asked.

"Small, small," he said, meaning, I assumed, for a few years.

"Are you from this village?"

"Yes, Missy," he said, still adding chips to the fire.

"Is your family living?" I asked.

The fire began to crackle. He stood up. "Yes," he said. "I a married man."

I was surprised. Despite his height he seemed quite young. Yet now that I stood nearer him I noticed his hands, worn from years of work. And as I studied his face I saw that his deepset eyes were older than those of a boy.

David went about his work at a slow yet deliberate pace. While he waited for the water in the black pot to boil, he filled a tub with rinse water from a rain barrel located under one end of the porch roof. Then he put hot embers from the fire in the big metal iron on the table under the shelter and began to try to press the dampness out of the clothes that he had washed a few days before, but which were not yet dry.

I watched him, hoping to find a way to reach him, to let him know that I wished to understand his way of life. But he kept busy, and he seemed sad and reluctant to talk.

Finally, feeling inadequate and frustrated because I could not seem to find any way to talk to this man, I turned away and walked a few steps beyond the yard to the edge of the woods. Standing there I noticed some green plants with large leaves specked with red. Then I saw that the woods were full of them, for they seemed to be growing wild.

"David," I called, "are these plants hearty?"

He left his work and came to where I stood. "What you say, Missy?"

"These plants," I said, "will they grow anywhere?"

"Yes, Missy," he said, "they grow like weeds all 'round."

"They are beautiful," I said, stooping down to touch one. "I'd like to plant some of them at the grave."

David was silent a moment, then he said quietly, "I help you, Missy."

Later when he had finished the laundry David came to the door. "We go now, Missy?"

The sun was shining as I stepped from the porch and saw that he carried on his head a large tub filled with the colorful plants. Balanced across the tub there lay a hoe and a shovel.

"David," I exclaimed, "you are weighted down. Here, let me help you."

I reached up for the tools. He stepped back. "Oh no, Missy," he said, "I take everything for you."

He remained adamant in his decision and we started off across the compound. I followed in the path that his steps made through the high grass. As we passed the schoolrooms a light rain began to fall. By the time we came to the old hut where Ma had once lived the rain was pouring down.

"You gonna get wet," he said, turning quickly and directing me to the open porch of the hut. I stood back under the protection of the thatched overhang. Standing in the downpour he lifted the tub from his head and put it on the ground.

"I fetch your raincoat," he said.

"No, David," I protested, "you will get soaked."

"It no matter," he said. He darted back down the path, his long blue shirt already wet and clinging to his body, his bare feet leaving large prints in the mud as he ran.

While I waited, a small boy came walking along and stepped from the path onto the porch beside me, a move which seemed almost incidental. Then I noticed the forked stick and the piece of rubber he carried in his hands. He leaned against the mud wall of the house and continued his effort to make a slingshot.

As I watched him I realized that his reason for joining me on the porch was not a fear of getting wet but was rather because the heavy rain prevented his seeing how to work on the slingshot. He had a smooth oval face and big black eyes, and he worked patiently.

Around the carved-out notch at the end of the stick he fitted a crude strip of rubber. He stretched the ends and tied them carefully, while he braced the stick against his chest. Observing the way he worked, slowly, deliberately, yet without undue concern, I thought of the fine line between patience and apathy.

Other people passed, a man carrying a long pole over his shoulder, a woman with a basket of cassava roots on her head. Each moved in the same slow pace through the rain. I thought of the patient, almost child-like qualities with which many of the people moved through their whole lives. Why in most of their actions did there seem to be a lack of drive, a lack of deep motivation? Why, for instance, did David believe that his only way to ever get a bicycle was to be given one?

I thought again, as I had the day at the church, about the history of tribal society. I remembered what I had learned about how each member of a tribe depends on his ancestral spirits, his family, his tribe, his chief to direct him and care for him. Then when the missionaries came the people learned to look to them for medicine, education, and spiritual guidance. In the days of tribal wars anger, greed, or revenge often drove them to conquest, keeping alive a vigor for life. But when wars were outlawed, the missions' vague and intangible promise of hope and heaven failed to fill the void which was left. Where could they find initiative and a chance to guide the destinies of their own lives?

David returned, bringing my plastic raincoat and hat, and an umbrella. By the time I put on the coat and hat the rain had slackened, so that David carried the umbrella the rest of the way, using it as a walking cane.

As we stepped slowly through the mud along the narrow path, I felt the eerie sensations of the jungle build up around us. The clouds blotted out the sun and cast a gloom of silence. The leaves and vines, overburdened by the rain, drooped as if beaten down unmercifully. The slippery logs, stretched precariously across rushing streams, seemed ready to toss us into the violent turbulence below. Rivulets of water fought their way into the dense jungle making green tunnels, mysterious with jagged roots, swelling, spreading into an endless flood.

I thought of all the wild creatures hidden in the deep bush to escape drowning. In the stillness I seemed to sense the trembling of life beyond. I fancied that I saw the fluttering birds duck their heads under their wings, and the frightened animals huddle in the snarls of limbs and leaves that were their homes. No light, no sound came from the bush which pressed on either side of us as we trudged through the high grass.

Gradually, as if I were being drawn into a mystic spell, I felt the sadness, the distress, the uncertainty of the jungle. And in the silence I seemed to feel the presence of some spirit that dwelled perhaps in a tall tree or in a rushing stream that we passed. For a moment it seemed easy to understand how the people of this strange land might come to honor such spirits, fear them, live under their direction in an unreal world.

But the physical effort needed as I pushed doggedly up the rutted hills was very real, and I followed after David, staring at his straight back, wondering how he managed to balance his headload burden. As the path wound on and on I wondered too what other burdens he carried in his heart.

When we came to the grave I began to hoe the weeds that

had sprung up in just the short time since my arrival in Sano-yea. With the shovel David dug holes for the plants. We worked quietly in a fine drizzle that began to fall.

I tried not to think about the reason for the grave, for while I knew the time that had passed since the death of my husband had not succeeded in healing my sorrow, just as time never completely succeeds in healing any profound loss, I also realized that quite some time had passed since I had demanded the answer for the WHY of life. Somehow I had found a peace with which to live and a way to follow the instincts and interests that led me along day by day. Besides, I reasoned that the tragedy of life is not death but rather what dies inside us while we are still alive.

Instead of dwelling on thoughts about myself, I looked at David and wondered about him. What peace was there in his humbleness? He bent down placing and adjusting the plants carefully. There was a gentleness in the way he pressed the dirt around each one.

He glanced at me, and in his eyes I saw a sad distant look. Yet in the quiet as we worked at the grave I felt a mood of reverence, of love, of the hope that sometimes dwells in the hearts of the patient, those like David, who are waiting, forever waiting.

If David spoke at all it was not louder than a whisper. And though I worked beside him I found that I could not say any of the things I wanted to say . . . David, what is it you feel as a human being . . . what are your hopes and dreams?

No, I did not speak. I hoed each weed, trying to ignore the fact that I left the roots behind where they would spring up again when I was gone and once more claim the grave.

While we worked, two boys appeared carrying a transistor radio. They wore tight pants and their faces were indolent as they stopped and stared at us. Raspy music from the station in

Monrovia jangled from their radio, as if lashing out at us, breaking the profound mood that had surrounded us.

David frowned at them and shook his head, but still they stood and stared. As I looked at them with a growing feeling of exasperation, their steady glare seemed to represent all the silent among us—those who, like myself at that moment, could not find the courage to speak out and communicate with another. And I realized that it is not enough to care about others in our troubled world. Some meaningful action is required. Something should be said. Something should be done.

But the two boys kept standing there with their arms folded. They did not offer to help. And I thought of all those who stand idly by, who ridicule by their silence, who never offer to help. The music jeered at us as if it were a haughty crowd looking on, scorning all that it did not understand.

Overwhelmed with frustration I could not stand it any longer. "Please," I cried, above the blaring sound made senseless by sharp static, "please, leave us alone."

They strode away then, as they had come, their tangled tune fading into the jungle behind them.

I sat down on a stone at the corner of the grave. The dripping rain ran down my face. I felt as if I had been flung from the present back to a moment ten years before when I had sat at this spot trying to find hope, trying to reason out a new faith and purpose for my own life.

And in that moment of sudden desperation I wanted more than ever to understand the people, the people like David who worked quietly, but perhaps *without* hope. But as I sat there I could not speak to him. I could not find words to reassure him that life has meaning, for I knew that words were not enough. Even a deep feeling of concern would never be enough. But what might help?

For a long time I stared at the damp jungle beyond. Finally I realized that the little girls, Marion and Rose, had appeared. They smiled at me, and then turning they ran back down the path leading to Ma's house.

A few minutes later Ma's daughter Mary came back with them, bringing an armful of lily plants. She nodded to me and without speaking began to set the plants out around the edges of the grave. I remembered what Ma had said, that if she were unable to set out the lilies her daughter would plant them for her.

Mary worked quietly and when she was finished she nodded again to me, her dark eyes still and sorrowful. And as if careful not to break the mood in which she had found me, she turned without speaking and taking the little girls by their hands she went back down the path toward their home.

I thought of the ways of communication, the acts of understanding, and I thought of the beauty of a deed done at the right place, at the right time. But how is one always to know what to do and when to do it, I wondered?

When David finished his work he too nodded to me, and picking up the tools and the empty tub he turned away in silence. I rose and followed him, still unable to speak, yet weary now from a feeling of more than frustration, a deep feeling of failure, a failure much greater than mine alone.

After we got back to the house I offered David some money in payment for his help. At first he refused. "Oh, no, Missy, I do for you."

"But David," I insisted, "I know you want to buy a bicycle and you can add this to your savings." I pressed the money into his hand.

He nodded then and closed his fingers over it. "I want bicycle," he said, and for the first time I saw a trace of a smile at the corner of his mouth. Yet as he stood there looking at me I felt that he had not completely given up the idea that somehow he would be given one someday.

"Do you understand," I asked, examining his trusting face, "why Sister Lena cannot give you a bicycle?"

His big black eyes blinked and he shook his head.

"She receives very little money for all the work she does here," I said.

"She does much work," he agreed.

"She works hard to bring better health to the people," I said, "but she cannot afford to buy them expensive gifts."

He hung his head.

"Besides, if she gave you such a gift," I went on, "all the other people who work for her might want something too."

He shrugged his shoulders ever so slightly, his bottom lip protruding like a disconsolate child. "She my Mama now," he said.

"But David," I said, "wouldn't it make you proud to be able to earn the money to do something like this for yourself?"

He looked at me, his eyes big and full of wonder, and I felt that never before had he seriously considered the possibility that he might do such a thing alone.

"I don't know," he said. But in the instant before he turned away I thought I saw a glimmer of light flash in his eyes.

I went into the house and sat in my room for a long time thinking of the complexity of the people. A people who, like David, willingly give so much of themselves, freely, without thought of payment. Yet trusting, believing that the good spirits, the Christian God, or the white Mama will provide the answers to their humble hopes or unrealistic dreams. How do people like that ever gain a more meaningful life? Where should help begin and where should it lead?

I thought of the children spoiled by the motherly nurse

about whom Sister Lena complained. "When they grew up," she had told me, sadly, "not one of them turned out well."

I pushed back the mosquito netting and lay across my bed thinking about this. No doubt the other nurse had been pressured by many difficulties and struggled to find a way to deal with the people. I thought of the many hardships in Sister Lena's life, yet she, too, went on trying to help the people in her own way. I wondered again how one best helps another.

I thought of the many comments I had heard as I traveled in other parts of Africa. Some Africans had said, "We do not want the advice of foreign experts, we only want foreign money." Others had said, "We are depending on the western powers for help but if they do not help us we will turn to the east for the things we want."

Their understanding of their needs and what could be done about them usually seemed to be in direct proportion to their degree of education. Yet even in the United Nations I had noted the groping of an educated African delegate, when he had said proudly, "Tell us what you will do for us and we will decide whether to accept or reject such aid."

Yes, they wanted a better life, and some Africans were planning and working in that direction. But independence alone had not necessarily brought it, as many seemed to have hoped it would. This disappointment on the part of the people had become increasingly clear to me in many of the new nations I had visited in Africa. The question remained: What was the best way the people could gain progress? All too often some other person, institution, or nation was blamed for the lack of accomplishments, or in some way held responsible for their future attainment.

I thought of the comments of the directors of the United States Agency for International Development projects and of the United Nations Specialized Agency programs I had visited in many parts of Africa. In a number of ways I had heard one basic question asked repeatedly. "How can we make the necessary aid reach *all* the people?"

What aid had reached the village of Sanoyea since my last visit ten years before? I had been told that teams from the World Health Organization had sprayed every hut in the village as part of a malaria control campaign. And there was Sister Lena's midwives' training program. These were remarkable advances, but what about the people, individuals like Ma, Gami, Steven, Duana, and David? Had there been any real help for them?

Beyond my door I heard David scuffing his feet in the hall. Bringing in the heavy buckets of hot water for the evening baths, he was going about his tasks with simple devotion, no doubt waiting, trusting that someday luck would bring him a richer Mama. Or was he beginning to think of ways he might do more for himself? Was there really some way to help these people take more responsibility for their own destiny?

Sixteen

"WILL YOU SHOW ME where Chief Kaine lives?" I asked some children who followed me the next afternoon as I went into the village.

They led me along the broad path through the center of town. We stepped over rain puddles steaming in the sun. Mud stuck to my shoes and squished between the children's toes. The villagers moved slowly about their tasks or stood idly beside their primitive huts.

I understood now what the chief had meant the day I arrived, when he said that many things had hardly changed at all. The apathy, the sense of waiting for something from outside to come in and bring an answer, was still there, reflecting itself in the attitudes of the people.

My visit was almost over. The mission pilot would arrive in a few days to fly me out the way I had come. Now as I walked through the village I wanted very much to know whether the chief understood the apathy of the people, and if so what he thought could be done about it.

"This the chief's house," said a little girl who stood beside me. We had stopped in front of a large square mud and cement house with a tin roof. I found the wooden shutters closed and the door bolted.

"The chief, he gone to Monrovia," said a tall boy in the crowd.

"When will he be back?" I asked.

"I don't know," he said. And all the children shook their heads.

I felt immediately despondent for I realized that I might never see the chief again nor know whether something could be done through him to help the people. I turned away, and as I walked along I noticed that the ruts in the path seemed deeper since the last heavy rain. I thought of how the lives of the people too were eroded, worn out with struggle. How could things ever be any better for them? What could the chief do?

Slowly I walked the full length of the village. My heart felt heavy with all I had seen and learned during my visit—the disease, the poverty, the apathy. The children seemed to sense my mood and they followed quietly.

A woman spread out her wash on the ground to dry. Another winnowed rice in a flat basket, while several others pounded cassava in their crude wooden mortars. An old man pulled weeds from his potato patch. A boy mended a fishing net. But most of the people stood silent and unoccupied.

They smiled at me as I passed, a flicker of joy coming and going instantly. I knew their friendliness yet I was glad no one stopped me to talk. My throat felt full and I could only nod to them. I walked on and on.

Beyond the far edge of the village I sat down on a large stone near a wide stream. I watched women come down the hill for drinking water. I saw them wade into the stream, fill their pails, and balance them on their heads. Then tediously they trudged back home. Others stood in the stream scrubbing clothes against a stone. One young girl, partially hidden by a limb, hummed a melancholy tune as she bathed.

A hunter came along the path, crossed the rickety log bridge, went around the bend, and disappeared into the jungle. I stared after him and remembered that that was the path and bridge over which I had entered and left the village ten years ago. The last time I crossed that bridge I had taken with me a new philosophy for my life, a new recognition of human rights, a new humility yet a new awareness of myself. Because of their interest, understanding, and ability to reach me, this was the gift the people themselves had given me.

The children stood in a semicircle around me now, their bodies naked except for the beads, strings, or bits of cloth they wore. Their little stomachs were puffed out with signs of malnutrition. Yet in their dear faces I saw patience, compassion even, for the "stranger lady" who must have looked bewildered.

The dense growth beyond us shielded out the sun as it slid down in the west. One by one the people finished their tasks. The sounds of splashing water grew still. Yet I could not seem to turn away, and the children stayed with me as if to protect me from the oncoming night.

Then in the dusk I heard footsteps on the bridge. I stood up and to my surprise I saw that it was Chief Kaine.

"Chief," I said walking to meet him, "I was looking for you, but I did not know you were returning today."

He nodded and we shook hands.

"I received a message that you are leaving soon," he said. "I have hurried back to say good-bye."

"How far have you come?"

"From Monrovia I caught a ride along the motor road to

Totota," he said. "I have walked straight through from there."

"But that's about seventeen miles of walking," I said, amazed.

"Yes," he said.

I studied his face and saw the simple kindness which was for him a way of life.

"You are weary," I said. "When you have rested will you come to the house and talk with me?"

"Thank you." He bowed. "I will come."

Later I began my conversation with the chief by asking about his family. "I had six wives," he said, "but now I have only four."

"What happened," I asked, distressed, "did two of your wives die?"

"No," he said, "I have decided to change my ways."

"How do you mean?"

"I'm gonna keep only my first wife."

"Why?" I asked. "Is it because of the rule of the mission?" I thought of former Chief Giddings and his story.

"No," answered Chief Kaine. "I'm thinking of running for the legislature from this district." He smiled. "And I notice that the government men in Monrovia got only one official wife."

"What will happen to your other wives?" I asked, thinking again of the sad story of the former chief.

"They are all young," he said, "and I have worked out a plan for them." He grinned sheepishly. "Maybe you think it a trick," he said, "but it the best way I know."

"Tell me."

"Well, it's like this," he said. "As chief I got to find work for young men in this area."

He folded his arms and went on. "If a boy come to me and

say he got no job, I send him out to a rice patch, sometime long way in the bush. He work four days for me, two days for hisself, one day he rest. I don't pay him but I got to care for him and his family if he got one, give him food, medicine, whatever he need, until he can make his own way."

"Do you have many such workers?" I asked, wondering what all this had to do with his wives.

"Yes," he answered, "right now I got 'bout twenty-five men and some of them very young and without wife."

He grinned again. "Sometimes I send my young wives out to cook for them. Then I wait for the natural things to happen."

He paused and laughed. "When the man comes to me and tells me that the woman gonna have his baby, I let him buy her cheap. She's happy, he's happy, and I'm happy."

"How can you be sure this plan will work?"

He threw back his head and laughed again. "It worked with two wives already," he said. "I think it will work for the others."

"Under the circumstances," I teased, "do you think it's fair to charge the men for your wives?"

"Oh, I got to do that," he said, his eyes wide. "Or my wives they feel awful bad if they think they worth nothing."

We sat in the living room as we talked. Rain had started to fall outside and a cool breeze blew in at the window.

"Where is your first wife?" I asked, remembering that I had found no one at his home.

"I took her to Monrovia," he said. "She is staying there with friends."

He clasped his hands. "If I am going to be in government work," he went on, "she's got to know how to act like a city lady."

I searched his face and thought of my hope that he might

have some plan for helping his people. "What about the problems right here in the village?" I asked.

"I hope I can help my people by being in the government."

"How do you think you can do that?"

"Well," he said, "seems like only the people in the central government got the power to get things done . . . like the road into Sanoyea they started. They promised that road years ago but nothing was even started to be done 'til now."

"Why not?"

"A government man owns a rubber farm near here. The trees are just now ready to tap for latex. He see he got to have a way to haul it out of here."

"But the people have needed a road for years," I said, thinking of all the head loads I had seen pass in and out of the village ten years ago, and of Duana's complaints about the movement of his own latex.

He nodded. "That's just it," he said. "We folks in the bush got to stir things up in Monrovia."

I felt discouraged as I thought of the complexity of the problems that he would face in Monrovia in trying to deal with a government run primarily by the coastal people. I remembered that as freed slaves from America the coastal people had captured and sold many hinterland natives into slavery. Finally taking a paternal interest in the villagers, the government had more recently begun to show national concern for all its people.

"Do you think you have a good chance of being elected?" I asked.

He smiled. "I think so. I am Paramount Chief of a large area."

"What are your duties as chief?" I asked, hoping that I could gain some insight as to what he might do for the people.

He stretched his legs and laughed as if he never had thought about his duties as such. They were natural functions known to everyone in his life.

"Well," he said, "I got to collect the taxes."

"How much do the people have to pay?"

"A farmer pays $5.00 a year plus forty pounds of rice," he said. "And a man without a farm must pay $5.00 a year plus $1.00 extra."

"How much is rice worth?"

"It sell here for five cents a pound, but we don't always have enough in the village for the man without a farm to buy all he needs. If he got to buy rice that's been shipped into Monrovia, he got to pay twenty-five cents a pound."

"What percentage of the taxes do you get for being chief?" I asked.

"I get 10 percent," he said, "plus 16,000 pounds of rice. The clan chiefs get 5 percent and 8,000 pounds of rice. And the town chiefs get their share."

"What else do you have to do as chief?"

His serious black eyes blinked as he talked. "I got to pay medical expenses for anyone who can't pay. I got to care for any children given me by parents who can't do for them."

"How many children do you have?"

"I have sixteen of my own," he said, "and eight of my brother's to care for, because he's a hunter and away most of the time. Then I have six more of these children who are homeless."

"That's a great many," I said, amazed.

He nodded. "Also I must have a hut and food for any stranger passing through the village," he went on. "And I got to have big entertainment for any government official who comes here."

"Sounds like you have a great deal to do."

"Oh, there's lots more," he laughed. Then when his face was serious again, he said, "Maybe my most important job is seeing about the people."

"How do you mean?"

"Investigating complaints, hearing palaver, and trying to be a fair judge."

"You must decide the cases yourself?"

"Yes," he said, "unless the fine is over $200, then I got to send the case to the District Commissioner."

"What kinds of cases have you had recently?" I asked.

He leaned back in his chair. "We had a man accused of raping a five year old girl," he said.

I thought of the innocent eyes of the little girl whom Sister Lena examined in the dispensary, and I remembered the despair in Steven's voice when he had said, "He just an old man, alone."

"Tell me about the man," I asked. "Do you think he was guilty?"

He shrugged his shoulders and hesitated before he answered. "I guess he was guilty."

"What punishment did he get?"

"We had to give him twenty-five lashes," he said, glumly.

I thought of Steven's plea for mercy and Sister Lena's effort to do what she felt to be right.

"We had another sad case last week," the chief continued. "A girl took her baby and met her lover in an old outdoor kitchen. While the man and the girl lay on their mat, the thatched roof fell in. They didn't get hurt but the baby, he dead. I hold them for murder."

"What will be their punishment?"

"As prisoners they got to work for six months to pay off their fine. And I got to fine the town chief of that village too."

"Why?"

" 'Cause it his job to see that all buildings in his village are safe, and won't fall down and kill people."

He leaned back in his chair as he talked and gestured with his hands.

"Suppose a prisoner pleads not guilty?" I asked.

"Oh, we find out if he's guilty."

"How?"

"We got the sasswood test."

"Tell me about it."

He leaned forward then, his eyes intent. "We heat a pot of palm oil until it's like burning grease. Then we drop a needle to the bottom of the pot. The prisoner has got to rub his hand with a mixture of crushed leaves. Then he's got to dip his hand in and bring out the needle. If he not guilty he won't get burned."

"Have you ever put your hand in boiling oil?" I asked skeptically.

"No," he admitted, "but I have given the hot cutlass test."

"What's that?"

"Well," he said, "I had a prisoner I thought was guilty but he say no, so I heated a cutlass 'til it was red. Then I dipped it into water. Next I stuck it in the ground. Then I hung a bag between two sticks. . . ."

"A bag?" I asked.

"Yes," he said, "a juju bag of magic medicines."

I nodded and he went on with his story. "Then I passed the cutlass under the bag. Then I put the cutlass against my skin to show it won't burn me 'cause I not the guilty one."

The chief curled his lips and spoke firmly. "Then I pressed the cutlass against the prisoner's arm. He was guilty and it burned him."

"Why do you think it happened that way?"

He shook his head. "I don't know," he said, "unless guilt

makes fear. And strange things happen to a man that's afraid."

"Yes," I said, and as we sat silent for a while I thought of the ways men everywhere react to fear. They some times seek revenge, deny the rights of others, stock pile armaments, provoke race riots, and often hide in the "safety" of an old idea.

Still I doubted the validity of these harsh tribal tests and finally I asked, "What does your government think of these kinds of tests for prisoners?"

"The government knows they are good tests," he said. "The Department of the Interior issues certificates to the chiefs who are allowed to give the tests."

I thought of how the people must accept this discipline as well as others imposed on them by the forces that guide their lives. "The people certainly have many problems."

The chief sighed. "I spend much time trying to get the District Commissioner and the government people in Monrovia to care about our problems."

Frowning, he shook his head and sank down in his chair.

I studied his face and wondered to what extent he understood the overall needs of the villagers. Did he sense their apathy? Still hoping that he might have some specific plan for helping the people, I asked, "What do you consider the greatest problem of the people?"

"We are all poor," he said. "We need more money."

"How do you think you might get more money?"

He thought for a moment, his frown wrinkling his face. "I don't know," he said sadly.

I realized then that he had only a vague idea of how he might get help someday through the central government. Apparently the tribal authorities offered little hope of real progress for the people, and perhaps because he was overwhelmed with his many duties even the chief had no plan of his own.

I felt exasperated and as I sat forward on the edge of my chair I found myself asking, "Do you think there might be some way something more could be done *now?*"

He hesitated before he answered, his eyes revealing the same silent searching look I had seen on the faces of many people. "I don't know," he said finally, "but it would be very good if we could find a way."

Seventeen

ALL THE NEXT DAY I walked about the house, the compound, the village, down the path over which I had been carried by the hammock boys, and back along the path leading from the grave. Finally, late in the day, I went to see the Andersons. They were a friendly intelligent couple and I felt sure Sister Lena was right when she said that they wanted to help the people. Perhaps they might help me see the full complexity of the people's problems.

"What do you think is the greatest need of the people of Sanoyea?" I asked Erwin, as I sat across from him on his porch. Marcia had gone into the village to shop, and I found him studying.

He was dressed casually in a grey sports shirt and pants, and he held a book on his lap. He sighed, closed his book, and leaned back. "I guess they need just about everything."

I waited, but when he did not pursue my question any farther I asked, "What is your main task here?"

"The mission board wants me to learn the language before I do anything else." He sat forward and showed me the Kpelle study book he held.

"It's a tonal language, not easy to learn," he went on. "I'm supposed to be able to speak it by the end of a year."

I glanced through the book. "Didn't you tell me that you are a farmer?"

"Yes." He nodded. "I'm the first farmer our mission board has ever sent to Liberia."

"What will you do after your language study?" I asked.

"I'm not sure," he said. Then motioning beyond the screen he added, "But I've started one thing already." He stood up and pointed toward the side yard. "See those chicken coops I built."

I rose and stood beside him.

"I had some chicks sent over from the States," he said. "And I'm trying to prove that they will live here."

I looked through the screen at the pens built high off the ground. Each of the legs of the pens stood in a tin container.

"Those tins hold poison," he said, "to ward off rodents, ants, and snakes. If I vaccinate the chickens and feed them properly I might improve the poultry stock around here eventually." He grinned. "That is, with a little luck."

"How do you mean?"

He sat back down and sighed. "It won't be easy to convince the natives."

"Why not?"

He ran his hand across his short cropped hair. "Some of the people have looked at the pens," he said, "but they say they have no money to build pens or to buy feed for their chickens. Not many people own chickens, and those who do let them run wild finding food wherever they can. Because of this the chickens are thin and almost too tough to eat."

"How can you help them understand?" I asked.

"I don't know," he said. "I offer to exchange one of my healthy chickens for two of their sickly ones. Of course I hope to show them how much I can improve their stock by my methods, and I hope they will use my healthy chicken for breeding purposes."

"Does anyone use an improved method for raising chickens?"

He rested his arms against the sides of his chair. "Miss Amanda does fairly well with a fenced-in area," he said, "but she often loses a chicken when some animal digs under the fence at night. I've been vaccinating her chickens lately. At least that saves them from disease."

The leaves of the mango tree at the corner of the porch threw dark shadows across his face as he talked.

"What else do you plan to do here?" I asked.

He leaned forward and pointed beyond the screen at two women going along the path carrying a small fishing net. "There are not enough fish in the streams," he said. "I'd like to build a pond and plant it with fish."

He shook his head sadly. "About the only source of protein here is wild meat and it's getting very scarce."

I thought of the gift of raw meat Duana gave me when I arrived in Sanoyea, and I remembered how proud he had been that he had made a kill.

From beyond the screen I saw two small children crossing the yard, their arms and legs thin and boney. They, like all the others, suffered from malnutrition because of inadequate protein in their diets.

"What about their rice, do the people grow enough?" I asked.

"No, they have hungry time every year before the new crops are ready."

"What can be done?"

"The land is so poor that highland rice can be planted on the same spot only once in seven years. This means the hard work of clearing a new spot of bush for planting every year."

He folded his arms. "Then the birds steal some of the seeds and come back again for the grains when they begin to sprout."

"That's terrible," I said.

He nodded. "And even worse, if the natives don't put up a fence of some kind the ground hogs will get most of their crops."

"This all sounds really hopeless," I said. We sat silent for a moment and I wondered how often he thought of the many hardships that the people suffered, how involved he had become in their lives, and in what way he was truly reaching them as individuals. But before I could ask, he went on talking.

"I think the people would get a better yield from lowland rice," he said, "but who can blame them for not wanting to wade around in water filled with disease and snakes."

I sat forward on the edge of my chair. "It seems to me," I said, struggling with the feeling that was becoming increasingly disturbing, "that something very basic is needed . . . some different kind of understanding."

Looking out toward the village he did not seem to hear me. "Neither medicine nor agriculture can solve all their problems," he said. "Even religion might not do as much as we hope."

Then he added, "But if the people will listen to me I might be able to help them a great deal."

Those words sounded strangely familiar, for I remembered that Sister Lena too had said them when she wondered why the people did not always heed her advice.

Marcia came in then followed by the pet Vatika. She carried a basket filled with papaya, sweet potatoes, and cassava roots.

"The natives boil these roots and then pound them to make fufu," she said, showing me the potato-like roots. "But I boil them and then fry them. They are almost as good as french fries."

The conversation turned to recipes and household chores, and it was quite some time before I found a chance to ask her what she thought might be done to help the villagers. As she answered she smiled at her husband. "I think Erwin will accomplish a great deal," she said proudly, "if he can make the people see what they ought to do."

"And how about you?" I asked, thinking of her training as a nurse and the many ways that knowledge might be useful. "What can you do?"

She frowned and I regretted that she seemed to feel that mine was a critical question. "I keep very busy," she said quietly.

Erwin sank back in his chair and seemed lost in thought. In the shadows of the porch a gloom settled on his face. "If the people don't want to listen to me," he said, "I guess they won't."

He rose then and paced nervously back and forth. Suddenly he stopped at the screened end of the porch and stared down the wide path toward the dispensary. From where I sat I saw that he watched Sister Lena, her head held high, as she came out of her house and walked with purposefulness across the road and into the dispensary. Warily he shook his head, and I could only guess his thoughts as he turned away and sank down again in his chair. "I don't know yet," he said in a low exasperated voice, "just what I'll be able to accomplish."

When I left the Andersons' house I felt disappointed, despondent. I did not know which way to turn. I walked slowly across the compound and stopped finally to watch the school children who had assembled to clean the grounds, the paths, the classrooms, and the desk and benches. Their school would begin soon and they were required to complete these tasks before opening day. Some of them bent over, hacking away at the tall grass with short-handled knives. Others swept the paths with palm fronds, while the small boys carted away the trash in baskets woven of vine and limbs.

I noticed that an adult supervised each group of children. As I looked around I saw Miss Amanda with the girls who swept a path. She waved to me and I went and stood beside her while her students finished their work.

"Will you walk home with me?" she asked then. She seemed to sense that I wanted desperately to talk to someone, but that I did not know how to begin.

Her smile was reassuring, and I walked with her.

"What is the greatest need of the people?" I asked finally when we sat on her steps.

"Oh," she said with a deep sigh, "they sure need lots of things."

Heavy clouds rolled overhead and she frowned as she glanced up. "They need better roofs to keep out the rain," she said.

Then turning to me she went on. "They need more food, especially at hungry time. They need extra work that would bring in some money so that they could buy meat, milk, and the many things they need but can't grow or make. They need clean water."

She folded her hands and her dark eyes seemed to examine my face. "Maybe more than anything they need to learn ways to help themselves."

"Are they learning such ways?" I asked.

A bird darted down from a nearby palm tree in search of food.

"I started one thing," she said. "It ain't much but I think it helps a little."

"What did you start?" I asked, pleased by the sparkle that came into her eyes as she smiled.

She hesitated. Then staring out beyond the green trees to

the west she seemed, for a moment, to be absorbed by the mystery of the bright red glow that flowed across the sky from the waning sun.

"When I ring the bell tonight," she said, "will you come and see?"

I heard the bell right after supper and taking up my lantern I went out. Several women from the village came along the path. They too turned in at Miss Amanda's house.

The little dog Do-your-part met us on the porch. The bigger one named Lion let us pass after sniffing our feet.

Inside the large room that served as living and dining room, a few chairs stood against the walls. Across the room five women sat around a long table. The women who came in with me pulled up chairs and joined the others.

Miss Amanda rose and came to greet me. "Maybe this not much of a surprise," she said, "but I thought you might like to see the ladies learning how to sew."

"Thank you for letting me come," I said.

She smiled. "Maybe it not such an important thing, but I think you will understand."

Her eyes were gentle as she led me across the room. The women rose and greeted me. "Thank you plenty for coming to see us," one of them said.

I recognized some of the women as ones I had seen in the dispensary, at the church, or in the village. Also Gami was there and she held up the dress she was making for me to see.

"Gami," I exclaimed, "I didn't know that you could sew."

"Oh yes, ma'am," she said proudly, "it best thing I do." And as she turned back to her work I noticed that the lines that usually creased her forehead were softened. "I think I finish my new dress tonight," she added.

A little woman smiled as she worked with slender fingers

fashioning a shirt for her son. "We happy we learn plenty from Miss Amanda," she said.

The others nodded in agreement. The light from a lantern, which sat in the middle of the table, traced soft patterns across their gentle faces.

The eyes of all of the women seemed eager, yet only a few of them had work to do. One young mother nursed her baby. "I come to watch," she murmured.

Miss Amanda explained to me about the class. "A mission lady who once worked here sent us this box of cloth when she went home."

She put the box on the table and opened the lid. "This is the last piece of cloth," she said, holding up a length of brown and white fabric about a yard long. Two women stood up.

"My little daughter need a dress," said one of them.

"My baby boy too big for his only shirt," said the other woman.

Miss Amanda turned the cloth first one way and then another. Finally she spread it on the table. "I don't know," she mused.

Then she turned to me. "Do you think I can get two garments out of this?"

I shook my head. "I don't see how."

She smiled at the two women. "You are lucky," she said, "that your children are small."

Taking up an old pair of shears, rusty with years of use, she began to cut. "I've had these scissors since 1932," she said proudly.

Without a pattern she fashioned two simple garments out of the drab fabric. The women watched her carefully as she cut. Then threading their needles they set to work.

The door slammed, and looking up I saw that an old woman had come in. Her hair, beginning to grey, stood out from her head. She wore a simple print dress and in one hand she carried a jungle knife.

"I hear you got new way to cut," she said to Miss Amanda.

"Yes, I use scissors," said Miss Amanda, as she showed them to the old woman.

The woman picked them up and looked at them curiously. "I cut out my children's clothes with this," she said, putting her jungle knife on the table.

The other women giggled. They used such knives in the field, but before coming to the sewing classes they had wrapped cloth around themselves and most of their children had gone naked.

"Will you show me how you cut out a garment with that knife?" I asked.

The old woman agreed and Miss Amanda searched about in a box of scraps until she found a piece big enough to cut.

From a bag tied at her waist, the old woman took out a smooth stick. It looked like a piece of swamp reed. She wrapped the fabric over the stick and pulled it tight. Then she took up the jungle knife and with hacking strokes she cut along the stick, using it as the guideline.

Soon the tiny strip of fabric stretched around the stick fell to the floor. The edge of the scrap she had cut was surprisingly straight.

"Would you like to learn to cut with scissors?" asked Miss Amanda.

"Oh yes," the woman said, "I like to learn much more how to cut and how to sew."

Miss Amanda smiled. "Welcome to our class." Then she added sadly, "We don't have any more material, but there are still a few scraps here. You can begin right now to learn to cut."

The woman examined the scissors again. Her eyes sparkled as Miss Amanda showed her how to fit her fingers into the handles.

As the old woman struggled with her task the other women watched her and urged her on. When finally she cut across one scrap, she bobbed her head and giggled. Immediately she took up another scrap, a new confidence on her face.

A child from the adjourning dormitory room came in and whispered to Miss Amanda. I glanced at the doorway and saw all the older girls waiting together. They varied in size but each wore a simple cotton dress and barefoot rubber sandals. Their tiny stiff braids stuck out from their heads and they looked at me from quiet faces.

Miss Amanda nodded to the child and smiled. "The girls want to sing for you," she said to me.

I went into the next room where they had set out a chair for me. They crowded around, sitting on boxes and packing crates normally used for tables. Shyly at first they began to sing hymns in English and then others translated into Kpelle.

When I asked them to sing a tribal song they seemed surprised. "We never know white lady who want to hear our music," said the tallest girl.

All the girls giggled and with new luster they began to sing. Both the tunes and the Kpelle words seemed strange to my ear but they sang on and on, their voices clear and beautiful, their hearts full of the joy of giving.

Finally Miss Amanda came to the door. "It is getting late," she said gently.

The girls said good night and went to bed. A few moments later I looked into their crowded dormitory room where double-decker beds lined the walls. Most of the girls were already asleep. The tallest girl lay in the bed nearest the door. In the dim light I saw a smile at the corner of her lips.

As I went back into the other room, I thought of the gratification that comes from giving. Perhaps Miss Amanda had been able to gain her kindly, tranquil acceptance of life because of what she was doing for these children and for the women.

When the sewing was finished and it was time to go, the women gathered up their work and I took my lantern and walked with them. Miss Amanda followed us out and called to the women from the porch. "If I ever get any more cloth I'll ring the bell to let you know. Now don't forget what you learned, 'cause you all doing fine work."

The women smiled and in the soft lantern light I saw a different joy, an expression in their eyes which seemed to me just the opposite of the suffering I had seen so often on the faces of the people. It was an expression of satisfaction at having accomplished a task designed to help them help themselves. With dignity they waved to her and started ahead of me down the dark path.

I put my hand on Miss Amanda's shoulder and thanked her for letting me see what she was doing. She smiled but she shook her head. "What I do is only small thing," she said. "But I know that sometime, someplace, *everybody* got to find out who he is and what he can do."

After I left her and walked along with the dim lantern light swinging beside me I thought of what she had said, and I knew she was right.

Eighteen

LATER THAT EVENING as a heavy rain crashed against the roof, I lay in the dark on the porch lounge thinking of the people. Sister Lena, the Andersons, Pastor Bypou, and Chief Kaine had their own difficulties, yet they each wanted to help the villagers. But they all seemed to feel the need to *guide* the people rather than encourage them to find and solve their own problems. Even the memorial dispensary, I realized now, was something done *for* the people rather than *with* them.

Only Miss Amanda had found a way to motivate some of the women to help themselves. Was this why they had responded with such enthusiasm to her simple sewing class?

Lost in my thoughts and perhaps deafened by the sound of the rain pounding on the roof, I did not hear Sister Lena come out on the porch. When I looked up she stood beside me, silhouetted by the dull light from the living room behind her. She held something in her hands. "I have intended giving you this gift," she said, "for your son."

I sat up and took what she gave to me. She stepped aside and the light shone on the object in my hands, a piece of bright metal. I turned it around and saw that it was a cross.

About eight inches high, it was crudely fashioned and attached to a solid base so that it might stand upright on a table.

"It's kind of you to think of my son," I said, examining the cross, mystified as to her reason for giving it to me.

"I had some of these made for gifts," she said, "and I thought your son especially should have one."

I looked at her, still surprised.

Watching me for a moment she asked, "I don't suppose you recognize the metal?"

I shook my head.

She sighed and sank down in a chair. "One day a man came to the door," she said, speaking slowly and gazing out into the dark beyond the screen. "He had some metal pots and spoons for sale."

She pushed a strand of hair back from her face. "I could see that they were crudely made and I asked him if he had fashioned them himself." She turned to me and nodded. "He had. Then when I asked him where he got the metal, he hesitated at first but finally said, 'There are still bits of the metal bird up there on the hill where it fell.' "

She paused and shook her head. "I was amazed," she said, "that after all these years anyone still searched around in that plane wreckage."

She studied my face, but I turned away toward the black night and listened to the rain.

"I told the man that he shouldn't be wasting his talents on pots and spoons," Sister Lena went on. "I suggested that he make some crosses. I bought a few and I told him to sell the rest of them in the village."

She sighed again. "It seemed to me," she said firmly, "that these people ought to have some symbol of their Christian religion. Maybe then they wouldn't be tempted to turn back to their pagan ways."

For a while she sat in silence. No light or sound of any kind came from the village. No one moved along the path. No drumming could be heard. The bird calls that tore the black nights during dry time were stilled now by the raindrops which fell in a deluge from above.

Long after Sister Lena went to bed I lay there unable to rise. The humidity pressed around me, but a feeling of despair too seemed to weigh me down. Even the cross, which I still held, seemed heavy.

The rain slashed again and again at the roof as if it would never cease. I remembered being told that a rain such as this fell the night of the plane accident, beat down on the faces of the dead and the dying. I thought of the hill and the endless pieces of metal, large and small, that I had seen there ten years before, the remains of the wreckage. And as I held the cross I felt cold.

I thought of the meaning of the cross, of the meaning of the life of Jesus, of the love that He tried to teach, of the respect for human dignity that He constantly stressed in His short lifetime. I thought of the cross as the symbol of Christianity, how it is meant to remind all Christians of the sacrifice made for them that they might be saved, and how it is meant to remind them also of the glory of the resurrection. I knew that within the body of the church this fellowship of suffering is meant to provide a continuous redemption, the bond that unites and the spirit that sanctifies.

Yet the cross also reminded me of the inhumanity of those guilty of the crucifixion, the sinful nature of man, the need for humility and sympathy, the anguish and suffering of Jesus and all those before and after Him who have suffered.

I realized suddenly that whenever I have looked at a cross I have always felt downcast. I have wanted to weep. How many other people respond to it with a similar feeling of despair rather than one of hope, I wondered?

As I touched the outline of the piece of metal I held, I

thought too of the look I saw in the faces of the people of Sanoyea as they came out of the church where they had been admonished for their sins. I thought of the look of helplessness on the faces of the women in the dispensary when they were scolded for stuffing their babies. I recalled the expressions worn by the Moslem patient and by Duana when they had felt offended. I thought of Gami and Ma, both of whom felt falsely accused. I remembered the sadness in Peter's eyes as he told me his story. Yes, the people suffered in many ways, yet perhaps Comfort's mother was right when she said that the suffering that comes from a broken spirit is the deepest suffering of all. In the dark I held the cold metal cross against me and wept.

At breakfast the next morning my eyes returned again and again to the bulky cement cross that protruded from above the fireplace. I had wondered before why the builder had set it permanently into the wall. Finally I asked Sister Lena.

"I don't know," she said. "Perhaps the builder thought it was a decoration that would please all missionaries."

Gami brought in a plate of toast. She wore her new dress and she smiled at me. She put the plate on the table and without speaking she returned to the kitchen. Sister Lena took up a piece of the toast, grimaced at its burnt edge, and went on talking about the cement cross.

"I often think," she said, "that our own people should not have to be reminded constantly of the symbol of their way of life. One should be a good Christian anyway."

"You have your silver cross," I said, indicating her only piece of jewelry, which she always wore on a long chain at her neck.

She smiled her wan smile. "Yes," she said.

Without further explanation she soon rose and left me. I

watched her from the window as she walked to the dispensary and I saw the long line of patients waiting in front for her. She moved slowly, looking oppressed, I thought, with her cross hanging from her neck.

I thought of how every religion calls upon its believers to make some sacrifice, whether it is a material sacrifice to an altar, a direct action sacrifice of service, or a selfless sacrifice of deep concern for one's fellow man. I thought of how necessary it is for everyone to have some meaning for his life, whether it is a religion on which he leans, an ideal toward which he reaches, or a devotion to truth for which he is willing to search.

I thought of how man some times moves from one religion to another trying to find a better expression for his ultimate concern. I wondered what it means to each human spirit to move from one belief to another. I knew that for each individual the lonely search and the pain or the reward could be quite different. I remembered that in this village ten years before I had moved beyond my dogmatic religion of the past, which had not upheld me in my time of grief. I had been able to reach out for life anew because the gentle people with their compassion had taught me a new sense of empathy. And this had given me courage to appeal to reason, to search for a new way to live.

I thought of old Chief Giddings and what his conversion to a new religion had meant to him. I thought of all the people of Sanoyea. I seemed to see them grouped together as they had been when they danced that first day I arrived. I remembered what seemed to me the reason they danced, as if it were a symbol of their frustration.

I began to think again of symbols, of how they grow out of an individual or group need, and how they die when the belief or the situation changes. I wondered how many religious symbols had vanished from cultures where whole populations had been converted? I thought of how throughout history man had devised various kinds of symbols to identify himself with one group or prejudice himself against another. I thought of ideograms besides the cross—the star of David, the Buddha, the Tao symbol of the Yang and the Yin. I thought too of the eagle, the olive branch, the hammer and the sickle, the flags of different lands. I thought of the distortion and ambiguity in the use of some symbols, black signifying evil and white, purity. Yet there are the black veils of mourning and the white robes of the Ku Klux Klan; the bells rung sometimes for gladness and some times for sadness. I thought of the many, many symbols, especially religious and political symbols, that bring hope to some, despair to others.

I realized that the dispensary, a memorial to the dead, had become something of a symbol to me, for I had gained courage from my belief in the help it would offer the living. Yet now I thought of the grave. I recalled my frustration the day David and I worked there, when the boys had stopped and stared at us. The raspy sound of their radio had torn the mystic silence and hurled me into a mental confusion of indolent individuals or arrogant crowds—condescending or hostile, curious or indifferent, critical though inactive—a confusion that seemed to shatter pretense and make me face my inadequacies and those of all mankind in our communication with each other.

For a long time I stood at the window. From down the path I saw a child come along carrying a pail of water balanced on his head. Two women passed with babies strapped to their backs. An old man trudged along, a ragged fishing net in his hand. Each moved with his usual lethargy, revealing the apathy that is often the result of an anguished heart.

And as I stared out, the people on the path seemed to become all the peoples of the world, no matter what their color, their size, or their burden, all the people who live imprisoned in the confines of a broken spirit.

As I watched they moved on and on as if through the aeons of time, led by the little child who walked carefully balancing the bucket of water on his head. Their number grew and there seemed no end to their line. Their black eyes, their blue eyes, the grey, the brown glanced back, sending to me, like millions of drum beats pounding noiselessly in the air, a silent message.

The message seemed to plead for hope, hope that man would find a way to forsake all earthly symbols that set him apart or prejudice him, and that he would replace them with new symbols, especially ones that show a concern for human dignity. And the message seemed to beg for a chance for individuals everywhere who strive to be something more tomorrow than they are today.

Suddenly, I heard my voice speak aloud. "Is it in man that we find the ultimate symbol?"

"You talking to me?" Gami asked.

In my reverie I had not heard her come in from the kitchen. I turned and saw the question there in her dark eyes.

"Yes," I said, the vision of the endless line of humanity still moving before me, "you, myself, and all the others."

Epilogue

FIVE YEARS HAVE PASSED since my return from Sanoyea, since I last watched the work in the memorial dispensary, stood beside my husband's grave, said good-bye to Sister Lena, the Andersons, Ma, Duana, Gami, Chief Kaine, and all the villagers.

During those years I have begun to better understand the larger lesson learned as a result of my travels through Africa and my revisit to Sanoyea. I have tried to learn more about the broad concept of community development, that nebulous idea built on the theory of self-help. I have read voluminous documents, pamphlets, and books on aid to the developing countries. I have been in contact with the Community Development Foundation and other foundations, CARE, the African-American Institute and other private agencies, United States Agency for International Development, the Peace Corps and other government agencies, the United Nations and its major Specialized Agencies, and numerous religious groups and private industries with overseas interests. As a result of all this study I have gained new hope.

While some of these organizations are financing projects the effects of which will remain for years quite remote from the average person, others are constantly moving closer to the idea that the most essential, the most lasting, and the most appreciated assistance is that in which the individuals most immediately concerned participate.

In the meantime life has moved on in Sanoyea. Miss Amanda wrote that a church women's group to whom I spoke sent a box of fabric, needles, and scissors to encourage the continuation of her sewing class. "I rang the bell," she wrote, "and the women came running."

I learned that more Peace Corps volunteers are going to Liberia every year. And now many different youth groups in the United States are working at odd jobs to raise $1,000 to buy supplies to help build a Peace Corps school wherever a volunteer finds villagers willing to do the work themselves. Hopefully someday one of these will replace the hut in Sanoyea where Comfort and many other youngsters who cannot attend the mission school can begin to get a better education.

Marcia wrote that she was teaching a class at the mission school now, and that Erwin had installed an incubator and was raising baby chicks, hoping that the people would learn more about the care, feeding, and crossbreeding of their scrawny flocks. Also he is raising rabbits, has started several swamp rice demonstration projects, and hopes to make various vegetable seeds available to the villagers.

Sister Lena wrote that the wheel chair arrived and was put to good use in the dispensary before she had been transferred to the mission hospital farther back country. There she had found an opportunity to greatly expand her midwifery training program. "What I began in Sanoyea," she wrote, "is only a small part of the tremendous challenge facing the mission."

But during all these years since my return from Sanoyea I have tried to find a way that some far-reaching self-help program might be undertaken by the people themselves. After many frustrating attempts to arrange for a community development leader to be sent to Sanoyea to encourage the people to tackle their own problems, I had to give up that idea. Then I tried to arrange for some villager from there to go abroad to be trained in the techniques of promoting self-help projects. For many reasons this idea too proved to be impossible.

Now at last a workable path seems to be opening. Mr. Fred Hamilton, a Senior Program Officer in the UNICEF office at the United Nations, has informed me of an agreement recently reached between UNICEF and the Liberian government as a result of which a training school has been established in the Gbarnga district in which Sanoyea is located to teach women leaders from surrounding villages. These trainees return home to instruct the local women and girls in such improved methods of home making as the proper diet and care of babies, the need for boiling the drinking water, and many other basic aids for better health and prosperity.

The experience of the first year has been very encouraging, Mr. Hamilton reports. Some eighteen village leaders have been trained, of whom five are of a senior level. It seems that they are already making a noticeable impact upon village women. Some are also teaching simple homecraft, by invitation, to junior high school girls. The far-reaching effects of such teaching cannot be measured.

The future of the training scheme is still uncertain, Mr. Hamilton warns. There are not yet sufficient teachers to serve. Proper selection of women with leadership ability must be made in each village. More respect for women must be gained from the tribal officials, for the local governments must come to understand that the basic needs of the village can best be filled by women in such areas as nutrition, sanitation, and child care. And the local governments must be willing to pay the returning trainees for their continued services to the villagers.

Despite all the uncertainties I have greater hope than ever, for if this is successful it will not be just a remote attempt in the one village of Sanoyea (which was all I had dared to hope for). Instead it will involve what is really needed, a new mood of progress, a new motivation among the people throughout the area to take up many new ways designed to help them help themselves.

The District Superintendent, with the help of Miss Amanda, has already selected a woman trainee from Sanoyea to be sent to the new school. As Miss Amanda writes, "The time is right for this. The road into our village is almost finished and there is a feeling of expectation and new hope among the people."

Yet I know that if this whole effort were to be *tremendously* successful it would be only as a tiny stone dropped into a sea of sadness. Many, many such stones will be needed to displace the sea and rise up as an island of widespread hope. But the work has begun, not only by UNICEF but by the many other agencies and nations who are striving to keep alive the "new hope" of the people. Directors of many of these projects are facing the fact that not all aid, indeed perhaps not even the most effective aid, can be given at the top level. For in the end (or maybe more significantly, at the very start) it is the individual who must be reached. Thus in the years ahead all over Africa and even in the most remote areas of the undeveloped world, people will learn more ways to help themselves.

Can we dare to believe that man is entering a third stage in his relationship to his fellow man, having moved beyond slavery and the worst phases of colonial and religious subjugation? Now there are many signs, through the United Nations, through the gaining of independence of new nations, through the mutual fear of nuclear destruction, through the new attitudes of many of the religious missions, through the great expansion of the various forms of economic aid, of man's entering a new era, one of real respect for individual dignity. For if our ultimate symbol is *man,* then self-respect and respect for our fellow men are linked inseparably. One cannot be believed in and lived without the other.

Arnold Toynbee, the noted historian, has said, "Our age will be remembered chiefly neither for its horrifying crimes, nor its astonishing inventions, but for its having been the first age since the dawn of civilization in which people dared to think it practicable to make the benefits of civilization available for the whole human race."

Yet massive government projects handed down to the people will fail unless the people understand and want to participate. Even in our own towns and states, handouts to depressed areas, civil rights legislation, slum clearance, population control studies, governmental attack on poverty—none of these can truly succeed without proper understanding by and motivation of the people involved.

Everywhere I go I ask people, "What motivates a man to care enough to help himself?" Almost everyone gives me the same answer, "I don't know." Yet all those who have seen successes in community development know that there is *something* that works. Perhaps Dr. Waldemar Nielsen, president of the African-American Institute, gave me the best answer. He too began by saying, "I don't know for sure." Then he added, "But I think that if you give a man a chance that requires something of himself, and you find a way to help him understand the value of that chance, he will usually take it up and make it work."

I realize now that the eyes of despair that have haunted me these many years are not just the eyes I saw in Sanoyea. They are not even limited to Africa. They are the eyes that we all know, regardless of race or nationality, the eyes that tell of injustice, or of the indignities suffered deep in the human soul.

But I believe that wherever human dignity and hope are linked, therein lies the power and the impetus for the growth of humanity. Today a dream from the heart of man is spreading, stirring us, shaking us from complacency—a dream that may be destined to involve us all, for we can no longer stay isolated one from the other.

Sanoyea seems very close to me now, only a few hours away by plane. And I am excited by the prospect that in my lifetime, or that of my sons', man may gain ever greater recognition of the true value of human beings. Perhaps my ability to believe in such a better future stems partly from my need to shed the inherent feeling of guilt handed down from my slave-owning forebears. Yet it seems quite reasonable to me that many of the rebel gentry, long buried in the old family cemeteries of the South, might understand and approve today's concept of brotherhood, if they were given the insights and conditions of our times. For they lived the tragic years from glory through defeat. They too suffered broken spirits and loss of self-dignity. Those who followed them, some of whom still fight today the struggle for survival with bitterness and prejudice, might wish to consider their own potential rather than their fear, for each man, on the foundations of his own sufferings and joys, can help build for all mankind.

Perhaps then each of us must find his own way to help lift the burden of the silent message seen in the somber eyes of people here and everywhere, so that some day it can be replaced by a new gleam of hope.

About Elizabeth Bowne

Lecturer, traveler, researcher, active participant in U.N., church, and civic organizations, as well as homemaker and mother, Mrs. Bowne nonetheless finds time for completing her many writing projects because "I like people and sharing ideas." A native of Georgia, where she grew up on a plantation which had been in the family 125 years, Elizabeth Bowne is, however, fascinated by other lands. She is a regular lecturer at the United Nations Association–U.S.A. Communications Center in New York. She has traveled extensively in Europe, the Middle East, Africa, Central and South America, as well as Canada, Mexico, and the U.S.A.

Mrs. Bowne's first book, *Gift from the African Heart,* published in 1961 and condensed in *The Reader's Digest,* movingly told the story of her first sad journey to the small Liberian village where her husband lost his life in a plane crash. Recently she returned from her fourth trip to Africa where she led a group of Americans in visiting U.N. Specialized Agency projects in Ethiopia, Kenya, Uganda and Tanzania.